Practical Antennas
for Novices

John Heys, G3BDQ

Radio Society of Great Britain

Published by the Radio Society of Great Britain, Lambda House, Cranborne Road, Potters Bar, Herts, EN6 3JE.

First published 1992

ISBN 1 872309 11 9

Cover design: Geoff Korten Design.
Cover photo: Gordon Allis, G0LRS.
Illustrations: Jean Faithfull, G0DCU.
Typography: Ray Eckersley, Seven Stars Publishing.

Printed in Great Britain by The Bath Press Ltd, Lower Bristol Road, Bath, BA2 3BL.

Contents

Contents

Foreword

Some strive for complete understanding of the theory of propagation and antennas. This is entirely commendable but often needs considerable skill in mathematics. Others learn as much as they can and eventually reach a state where they believe they understand. This all-important state is often achieved by practical experimentation.

In this book John Heys uses the immense wealth of his experience to guide the beginner along the lines of 'learning by doing' – the philosophy adopted by those engaged in training for the Novice Licence. Follow some or all of the designs, make changes and observe the effects, make notes of the changes and results, and quite rapidly a greater understanding will be achieved and, who knows, some as yet undiscovered design may be produced.

Keep experimenting, and good luck.

Ewart J Case, GW4HWR
RSGB President 1991

Chapter 1

Introduction and some antenna basics

The old name for an antenna was an 'aerial'. This is a word you will mainly come across in early radio (once called 'wireless') books and magazines, but it is still occasionally used.

A radio receiver will seem 'dead' if it is not connected to an antenna. You will not notice this effect with a domestic broadcast receiver which has been designed to tune the medium- and long-wave bands, for these sets usually have an internal antenna. This is a small tuned circuit having a coil wound over a length of ferrite (a kind of ceramic containing iron powder) material and is called a 'ferrite rod antenna'. These antennas are only efficient for receiving stations on the low-frequency (150kHz to 1.5MHz) broadcast bands.

Radio transmitters are also useless unless they are connected to a suitable antenna (ferrite rod antennas cannot be used for transmitting) and their effectiveness will be directly related to the antenna efficiency.

All sorts of antennas

Antennas come in a wide variety of shapes and sizes. An interesting exercise when travelling by road or rail is to note the many different antennas seen on the journey. A few of these are sketched in Fig 1.1 overleaf and they range from the mighty wire systems suspended from high lattice towers to the tiny 'rubber duck' antennas on many hand-held 'walkie-talkie' transceivers.

The size of an antenna is often related to the frequency (or wavelength) of the signals to be received or transmitted. Antenna wires or elements on HF or VHF (short or very short waves) are often a half or a quarter of a wavelength long. This means that on very high frequencies (ie very short wavelengths) antennas can be quite small.

The dish television antennas on homes have a very

tiny antenna arranged at the front of the curved reflector surface of the dish. This reflector gathers the signals and focuses them on the antenna unit.

A domestic dish antenna receives TV signals on a very high frequency. Such a dish scaled up to work on the Novice HF bands (between 1.95 and 51.7MHz) would be very large indeed. The 1.95MHz version would completely dwarf a tower block!

The half-wave antenna

In your students' notebook *Training for the Novice Licence,* Worksheet No 19 discusses tuned circuits and how they are used to tune to particular radio frequencies. These circuits may be arranged as either parallel or series tuners (see Fig 1.2) and they will each have an inductance (coil) and a capacitor to determine the tuned or resonant frequency. If a transmitter was coupled to a parallel tuned circuit very little of its power would escape and be radiated. However, if the coil was unwound and stretched out into one giant single turn, it could still be tuned by a capacitor connected to its ends (see Fig 1.3). Now if RF (radio-frequency) power was coupled to the circuit, a considerable proportion of that power would be radiated. The circuit has become an antenna.

There is a well-known antenna design of this type called a 'halo' which is used on the VHF bands by mobile operators. Unfortunately a halo would be very large if scaled up to operate on the lower HF bands (say from 1.95 to 10MHz), and even on the higher frequency bands such as 21, 28 and 50MHz the constructional difficulties make it impracticable.

If we now completely straighten out our single turn or loop and disconnect the capacitor, the length of wire is still a tuned circuit! The wire has self-inductance and also self-capacitance. The inductance and

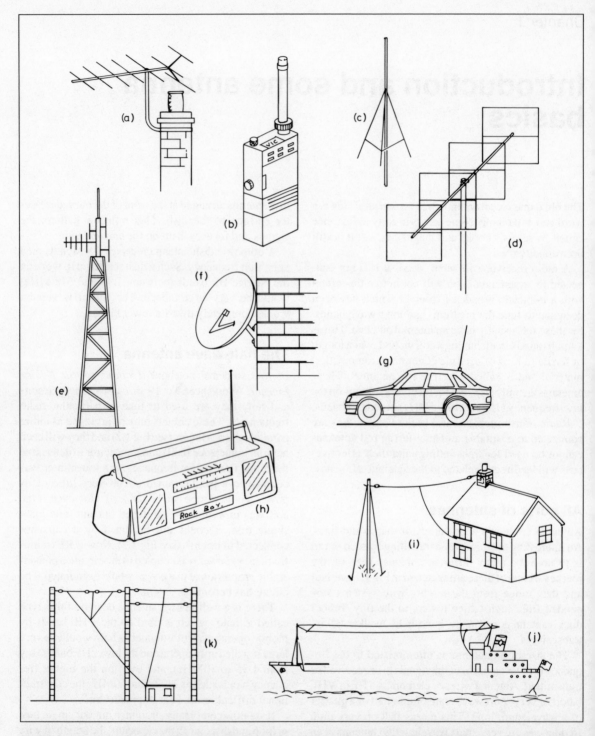

Fig 1.1. A variety of antennas. (a) Domestic TV. (b) Hand-held transceiver. (c) CB radio. (d) Rotary 'quad' beam, amateur or professional. (e) Public service point-to-point. (f) Dish for satellite TV. (g) Car radio, taxis or business vehicles. (h) Portable broadcast receiver. (i) Amateur wire dipole. (j) Ship radio. (k) Short-wave broadcast

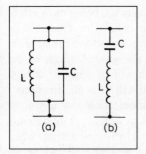

Fig 1.2. (a) A parallel-tuned circuit. (b) Series-tuned circuit. L is the inductance; C is the capacitance

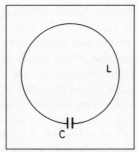

Fig 1.3. A parallel-tuned circuit pulled out to make a single turn or loop L tuned by capacitor C

capacitances will be small so the wire must be lengthened to compensate if it is to tune to the original frequency. It is now a basic 'half-wave' antenna. It is called this because to achieve resonance at a particular frequency its length must be approximately half a wavelength at the operating frequency.

Half-wave antenna length

In the early days, radios had their tuning controls calibrated in metres of wavelength and the frequencies of stations were not noted. It is quite easy to convert a wavelength in metres to its frequency in megahertz (MHz) by dividing 300 by the wavelength. A wavelength of 10 metres therefore will have a frequency of 30MHz. Conversely, to change a frequency in megahertz to a wavelength in metres we must divide 300 by the frequency. A frequency of 10MHz therefore will have a wavelength of 30 metres.

A half-wave wire, because it is in the real world with end capacitance (arising from end connections to insulators etc) and not in free space, must for practical purposes have its length reduced by about 5% to be resonant on its design frequency. If, instead of wire, the half-wave antenna is made from a thicker conductor, its length will be reduced by more than 5% to be resonant. This is important when making antennas for VHF or UHF (very high frequencies or ultra high frequencies) such as on the 433, 1240 and 10,000MHz bands.

To calculate the metric length of a wire half-wave antenna, 143 must be divided by the required frequency in megahertz. If you are still a 'feet and inches' person the length in feet can be found by the division of 468 by the frequency in megahertz.

It often happens that the garden area available is too small to accommodate a half-wave antenna for one of the lower HF bands such as 1.9 or 3.5MHz. It is then possible to put up a quarter wavelength of wire and compensate for the missing quarter wave by using a good earth connection or an arrangement of buried wires close to the ground (see Fig 1.4(a)). The latter system is called a 'counterpoise'.

Another way to make a short wire resonant is to include an inductance (coil) somewhere along its length. This technique is called 'inductive loading' (see Fig 1.4(c)).

More about half-wave antennas

The basic half-wave antenna and its special characteristics is the basis for almost every antenna design so it becomes important for the Novice to understand something about its special properties. When a half-wave antenna is positioned horizontally and used for transmitting, the electric field of radiation will be polarised horizontally. 'Polarisation' means that the waves peak

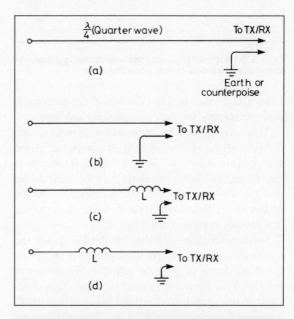

Fig 1.4. (a) A quarter-wave antenna wire with its earth or counterpoise wire to replace the 'missing' quarter wave. (b) This wire is shorter than a quarter wavelength and will not be resonant at the operating frequency. (c) A short wire can be brought to resonance by adding an inductance L in the circuit. (d) The inductance can be inserted anywhere along the wire. If positioned centrally or towards the unconnected end of the wire, L must be greater than that needed at (c)

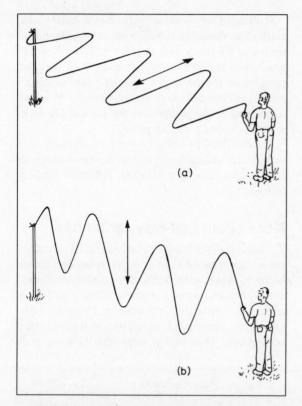

Fig 1.5. (a) Horizontally polarised waves along a rope. (b) Vertically polarised waves along the rope

from side to side in this case but if the antenna is positioned vertically they will peak up and down.

This is a very crude description of wave polarisation and perhaps the analogy of a length of rope tied at one end and held at the other will be clearer. If the rope is moved up and down regularly 'waves' will travel along it. They will be vertically polarised. When the rope is moved from side to side the waves will then be horizontally polarised (see Fig 1.5).

For long-distance working on the HF bands the polarisation of antennas for transmission or reception is not important because the refraction (bending) of the signals in the ionosphere changes any initial polarisation on a constantly varying basis. It is important, however, for short-distance 'ground-wave' propagation, especially at VHF, and for this reason TV antennas must be polarised to correspond to the polarisation of the transmitting antennas (see Fig 1.6 opposite).

A horizontally polarised half-wave antenna when positioned at least half a wavelength above the ground will show some 'directivity'. This means that it will

perform best in certain directions, being most effective at right angles to the run of the wire. There will be little radiation and poor reception from each end of the antenna. When closer to the ground, much of the radiation from the antenna will be upwards at high angles to the horizon and it will be in all directions.

For long-distance communication low angles of radiation are needed so it is as well to put the antenna as high as possible. A vertical half-wave antenna when positioned well above the ground will radiate all around and the radiation angles to the horizon will be small. If a vertical half-wave antenna is brought closer to the ground the radiation angles will increase and its effectiveness for long distance and for ground-wave communication will be reduced.

Antennas will not operate correctly if they are positioned close to buildings or trees for then they will be screened and their performance will be unpredictable.

Voltages and currents

Earlier in this chapter a half-wave antenna was likened to a resonant tuned circuit. This is true in the way the RF currents and voltages are distributed along its length. Each end of the coil in a parallel-tuned circuit at resonance, as shown in Fig 1.7(a), will have high RF

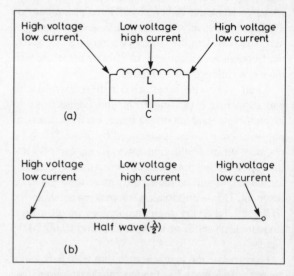

Fig 1.7. (a) A parallel-tuned circuit when at resonance has a voltage and current distribution as shown. The midpoint along the inductance L has a zero voltage but a high current. (b) A half-wave antenna has the same distribution of voltage and current as the tuned circuit in (a)

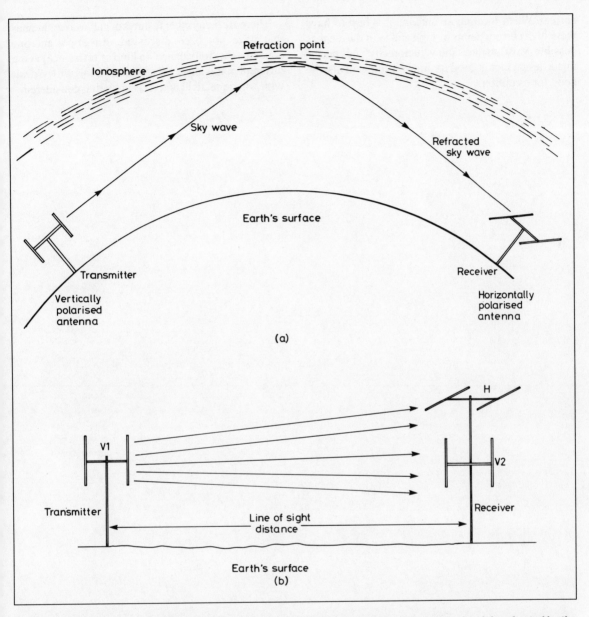

Fig 1.6. (a) The sky wave from the transmitting antenna on the left is vertically polarised but when it is refracted by the ionosphere the polarisation changes randomly and the horizontally polarised receiving antenna will pick up good signals. (b) For line-of-sight (or just beyond the horizon) propagation, the transmitting and receiving antennas must have the same polarisation. The higher antenna H at the receiving station would pick up weak signals from the vertically polarised transmitter antenna V1 but the lower antenna V2 would pick up strong signals

voltages which reverse in polarity during each cycle. The mid-point along the coil will have zero RF voltage present and it may be earthed without upsetting the operation of the circuit. The half-wave antenna shown in Fig 1.7(b) also has high RF voltages at each end and

these diminish towards the centre where the voltage is always zero. At the centre the current is highest and it falls away to almost zero at the ends of the antenna.

The radiation from a transmitting antenna (a half-wave or any other type) is greatest at the points of high current. When locating an antenna it is best to have these high current points as high and as in the clear as possible. Most antennas show 'reciprocity'; this means that a design that is good for transmitting will also be good for reception.

There are many other features of half-wave antennas that have not been discussed. An important one concerns the 'impedance' (a kind of resistance) at the different points along the antenna and this will be dealt with when practical antennas are being considered.

Chapter 2

Antennas for 3.5MHz

The frequencies for Novice operators on this band (the 80m band) are between 3.565 and 3.585MHz. This is a 20kHz allocation within the amateur CW section of the band. Unfortunately this band, although a primary one for amateurs, is also shared with other services such as military, commercial and point-to-point communications. This means that during the hours of darkness there may be considerable interference from high-powered, non-amateur stations.

The 3.5MHz band is useful for working with local and near European stations up to a range of about 600 miles (1,000km) in daylight hours. This range cannot be guaranteed for it will depend upon propagation conditions which change from day to day. There are times when solar flares and similar phenomena bring about radio 'blackouts' when only stations within the ground-wave range (a few miles) can be heard. Conditions also change with the seasons and they are generally better from the autumn through to the spring. During the hours of darkness it is still possible to contact European stations and the range will extend to about 1,500 miles. This will allow contacts over most of Europe and when conditions are particularly good with stations in other continents.

The recognised low-power (QRP) operating frequency of 3.560MHz is close to the Novice frequencies and no doubt many of the low-power fraternity will tune to your part of the band. Many QRP operators on 3.5MHz use powers of 1W or less and your 3W will certainly be enough to give you many contacts when using a simple antenna system.

Centre-fed half-wave antennas (dipoles)

Using the formula given in Chapter 1, the length of a half-wave antenna for this band will be exactly 40m

(or 131ft). This is based upon a centre frequency of 3.575MHz and it will cover the whole 20kHz Novice frequency allocation. The bandwidth of a half-wave dipole antenna is more than enough to cover this range of frequencies. The word 'dipole', by the way, describes an antenna that is in two equal halves, the total length being half a wavelength.

Few amateurs can erect their 3.5MHz antennas as high as a half-wavelength (40m) so their DX (long-distance) performance is limited, especially when using low power. This relationship between antenna height and low angles of radiation to the horizon was mentioned in Chapter 1. Antenna length restrictions imposed by the space available also face amateurs contemplating working on 3.5MHz. Fortunately the ideal 'unbent' half-wave antenna is not essential, and it is possible to re-arrange a half-wave dipole so that it can fit into an average-sized garden.

Fig 2.1 shows the ideal dipole arrangement and Figs 2.2, 2.3 and 2.4 illustrate how the antenna can be

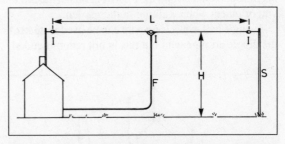

Fig 2.1. An ideal dipole for the 3.5MHz band. The total length L is 40m and its height above ground H should be also 40m. In practice this can be reduced considerably and the antenna will perform well when H is brought down to 20m. At heights below this most of the radiation will be at high angles to the horizon. The far support S may be a mast, a tree or another building. The coaxial feeder F must come down vertically from the centre of the antenna and then it can run along or be buried in the ground. The insulators I may be home made or obtained commercially

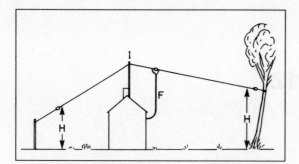

Fig 2.2. Here the rear garden is too short to allow a full half-wavelength of wire so most of one leg of the antenna is taken over the roof and dropped to a convenient tie point. The far end of the antenna goes to a tree or other suitable point and the height H should be as great as possible. This arrangement will give a good account of itself for the feed point where the maximum antenna current will be is well up in the clear. The antenna wire must be insulated from the chimney pole by insulator I

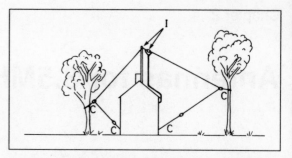

Fig 2.4. In an even more restricted space the dipole can be bent into a trapezoidal shape. This will reduce its effectiveness but it will remain a useful radiator because its centre point where the feeder is joined is at the highest point in the system. The insulator I insulates the wire from the mast and is necessary even when the latter is a wooden one

modified to fit into a restricted space. There will be a penalty for re-arranging the dipole and bringing it closer to the ground: it will tend to radiate at high angles, thus limiting the normal transmission range; there can also be absorption of RF energy by nearby buildings etc. However, it will still be a useful radiator and enable contacts with European stations even when using low power.

Another way to put up a dipole is to have it sloping down from a single high point and, when necessary, folding back part of the lower wire (Fig 2.5). When dropping or running back some of the dipole it is best to see that no part of it is less than 2m from the ground. If the wires are too close to the ground the dipole will become unbalanced and they may become a hazard to you or others when walking in the garden.

A single half-wave long wire can be used instead of the dipole arrangement but this is not recommended.

Reference to Fig 1.7(b) will show that the ends of the half-wave antenna are high-voltage points. This complicates their connection to a transmitter or receiver because a low-impedance feeder (usually coaxial cable) must not be connected to high-voltage, and therefore necessarily high-impedance, points. If the end of a half-wave wire antenna is brought into the operating room, the high-voltage/high-impedance it presents will make it difficult to match to the low-impedance antenna connections (usually 50Ω) of the equipment, and even when this is done, the presence of high RF voltages close to the operating position may produce feedback or instability problems in the equipment. When using high power levels 'end feeding' becomes dangerous and might result in RF burns to the operator should he or she accidentally come into contact with the antenna wire.

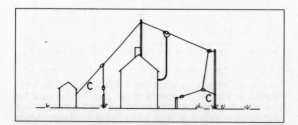

Fig 2.3. The dipole is arranged in a very small garden space in this example and both of its legs are dropped or bent back. The feed point is again positioned well up in the clear. The cords C are best made from the strong materials used for sailing boat ropes

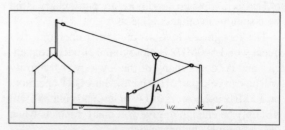

Fig 2.5. This dipole is the least efficient of those shown so far. Its mean height is low, a great deal of the far antenna leg is bent back close to the ground and the feed point is also very low. Although far from ideal, this antenna will nevertheless still radiate good signals over the British Isles and Western Europe. The section of wire A can run out away from the line of the elevated section of the antenna – indeed it is better if this is done so it will be well away from the lower end of the feeder

The centre of the half-wave wire is a high-current point and there it also has a low impedance. If the wire is cut at the centre, making the wire into a dipole, the impedance of the connection to the two wires at the antenna centre will be between 50 and 70Ω. The actual impedance depends upon several factors such as the height of the antenna, its proximity to trees or buildings and whether the wire runs in a straight line or is bent or doubled back.

Figs 2.1 to 2.5 show a connection to the centre of each antenna. This is the 'feeder' and it is normally a length of 'coaxial cable' ('coax' for short). A special twin-wire feeder may be used instead of coaxial cable but it may present complications at the equipment end and is not recommended for use by the Novice.

Coaxial cable is available in a wide variety of impedances and diameters but for low-power work an outside diameter of 5mm is suitable. One such cable, type RG58AU with an impedance of 50Ω, is ideal for the Novice. This cable has a stranded centre conductor, whereas type UR43 with the same impedance and diameter has a single wire centre conductor. The cheap low-grade coaxial cables that are used for some CB and TV operations must be avoided. These cables often have inadequate braid shielding and poor weathering characteristics. TV cable often has a nominal impedance of 75Ω, whereas amateur equipment is usually designed to operate with input and output impedances of 50Ω.

A practical dipole for 3.5MHz

The first task is to make a careful examination of the proposed site for the antenna and take a decision as to whether the wire will run in a straight line, be bent in some way or slope. Much will depend upon the location of suitable anchoring points for the wires well above the ground. Chimney stacks are useful, especially when they carry an additional short (1m) pole lashed to one side. Trees, buildings or a metal mast can be used. You will 'lose' some garden length when using a guyed pole or mast, for its guy wires must run out a considerable distance from the structure. Self-supporting poles make fine radio masts; ex-telephone poles are sometimes available from British Telecom. Many amateur masts came down during the storms of recent years and care should be taken to locate a mast where it can do little damage should it not survive extreme weather conditions.

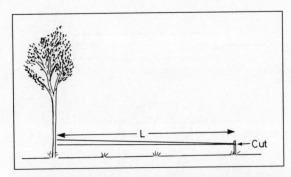

Fig 2.6. Measuring lengths of wire for antennas is an outdoor job and this figure illustrates the way to obtain two equal dipole legs. Before the stake is put in the ground a measure (rod or rope) must be used to determine L which is approximately a quarter wavelength at the operating frequency

Safety is all important when considering the location of antennas and their erection. It is best not to clamber on roofs unless trained and properly equipped for this task. The author employs the services of a professional TV antenna rigger who is quick, efficient and reasonably cheap! Some easy means to raise and lower the antenna must be arranged. This usually involves the use of pulleys. A visit to your nearest boating or yachting centre can provide good-quality weatherproof pulleys and the long-life ropes to be used with them.

The antenna itself must be made with copper wire and must not be so thin that it has little physical strength. Some amateurs use wire with an insulating covering and this works quite well for a time. Eventually, however, wind movements and swaying will weaken the wire and it may break inside its insulation and make repair difficult. Bare copper of the hard-drawn variety with a thickness of 14 or 16SWG is an ideal material for amateur antenna wires.

Measuring the two 20m lengths of springy copper wire is best done by arranging for two anchor points out of doors. A tree trunk, down-pipe or a stake can be used as one anchor and the second a sturdy wooden stake or metal rod set 20m away. A 1 or 2m rope or stick may be used to set the correct spacing distance and then it is an easy matter to fix one end of the wire to the first anchor and pull the rest out to the second point. Bend the wire back then to the original anchor point and you will have a 40m wire in two equal 20m lengths. Cut the wire at the far anchor point to get your two dipole sections (Fig 2.6).

The two outer ends of the dipole must have good

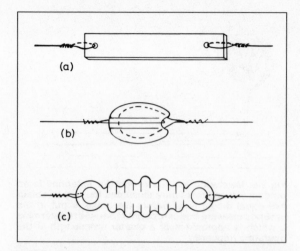

Fig 2.7. (a) An end insulator made from a strip of perspex or similar material. Your local glass supplier or 'glassworks' is a useful source of these materials and offcuts are very cheap. The insulator should be at least 130mm in length. (b) A commercial 'egg' or compression insulator. These items are available made from glazed ceramic, Pyrex glass or a plastic material. They will take an enormous strain force and, should they fracture, the wire loops prevent collapse of the antenna or an antenna support wire. (c) Ribbed strain or tension insulators can be found made from glass or plastic. The ribbing lengthens the leakage path between the end wires and weakens the surface tension of any water that falls on the insulator

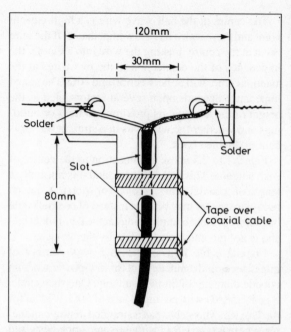

Fig 2.8. How to make the centre insulator of a dipole using a 'T' shaped piece of perspex or similar material. It is most important that the weight of the coaxial feeder does not pull on the connections to the dipole legs. The use of two slots cut into the vertical part of the 'T' and taping at two points will prevent metal fatigue at the soldered joints. The connections and also the top end of the feeder must be liberally coated with a moisture-proof material such as silicone rubber. Soldering the points where the antenna wires are twisted together at the top of the 'T' is not necessary

insulation to isolate them from the supporting wire or cord. Strong 5mm nylon or Terylene cord is available from DIY stores or yachting centres and is ideal for antenna supports, and will run easily through a pulley. If these materials are used instead of wire the antenna end insulators are not so critical and can be fashioned from strips of perspex or a similar material. Fig 2.7 explains how these are made and also shows the commercially made 'egg' and ribbed insulators made from Pyrex glass or a plastic material.

At the dipole centre, insulation is not so important because the RF voltages are very low and home-made centre connectors are adequate. One is illustrated in Fig 2.8. To prepare the coaxial feeder for its connection to the dipole centre, first carefully cut the outer plastic jacket (insulation) of the cable back for about 6cm (Fig 2.9).

The coaxial centre conductor and the braid 'pigtail' are soldered to the inner ends of the dipole legs and must be protected from weathering. This protection must also be given to the end of the cable to stop rainwater creeping into it by capillary action. There are many available products for sealing and the author

has over many years successfully used a silicone rubber material. This is transparent and is sold for sealing in bathrooms and kitchens.

The lower end of the cable must be fitted with a suitable connector. For HF work the PL259 plug is generally used and will connect to most commercial receivers and transmitters. Your Worksheet No 23(C) explains in some detail how this plug can be fitted to a coaxial cable.

Finally, before putting up the antenna a multimeter must be used to check that there is a low-resistance

Fig 2.9. An enlarged drawing showing how the inner conductor of the coaxial cable and its insulation are first prepared for connection to the dipole centre

connection between the centre pin on the PL259 and one leg of the dipole. The casing of the plug must also connect with the other dipole leg and there should be a very high, almost infinite, resistance across the plug from the centre pin and its outer case.

The feeder must, if possible, run down from the dipole at right angles for as far as possible and not run close to or parallel with either dipole leg. It may be convenient to run the cable along the ground to the operating position, or it can be safely buried.

Theoretically, an unbalanced feeder such as coaxial cable should not be connected directly to a balanced antenna, but in practice this will have little effect upon the antenna's performance. The 'free space' directional radiation pattern of a dipole (see Chapter 1) will not be realised when it is relatively close to the ground so any distortion of this pattern or 'squint' will not matter. When making dipole antennas or other antenna types for higher frequencies the effect of imbalance becomes a factor to consider and eliminate.

The completed dipole can be connected to your 3.5MHz equipment and there should be no need to adjust or 'prune' its length.

A three-eighth wavelength antenna

It may be difficult or almost impossible to put up even a 'bent' half-wave antenna for 3.5MHz, particularly if the garden is only about 20m in length. A quarter-wave wire tuned against the ground (to make up the missing quarter wavelength) might be used but this would have a serious disadvantage. This disadvantage is that the station end of the wire would be where the greatest antenna current and therefore the greatest radiation would take place. This part of the antenna would be close to the house and be badly screened whilst the far end of the wire, although up in the clear, would carry little current and contribute little to the radiation.

By lengthening the antenna to three-eighths of a wavelength (30m) it is possible to get the high-current point well up from the ground and away from screening influences (Fig 2.10). The RF voltages at the station end of the wire will not be high and a simple antenna matching unit (see later) will present a 50Ω impedance to the equipment. If the vertical section of the antenna goes up for about 10m the high RF current point will be up at that height and there will be effective radiation.

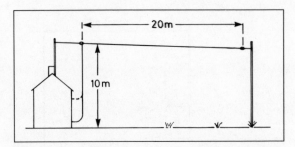

Fig 2.10. The three-eighth wavelength wire antenna is also sometimes called an inverted 'L'. When the vertical part of the antenna is about 10m long the high-current point will be well above the ground and surrounding buildings etc. This antenna can also slope towards the support at the end furthest from the house without much loss of efficiency. The vertical section is best kept well away from the wall of the building and it may enter an upstairs or lower window

This antenna does not use a feeder and, for some of its length, must actually enter the house. This part of the antenna must be kept as short as possible and a suitably insulated feedthrough must be provided. A hole may be drilled through a wooden window frame into which can be inserted the body of an old ballpoint pen of the 'BiC' variety. The antenna wire will pass through this and be kept from contact with the wood. Wood is a poor insulator at radio frequencies and it easily absorbs moisture. Should the window frame be made of metal, a hole through the adjacent brickwork can be made. This hole may require a longer insulating tube.

Some windows are made from a number of small panes and the replacement of one by a piece of perspex or similar transparent plastic will make the entry of antenna wires an easy matter; just a small diameter hole is needed and no other insulation. In the worst scenario, when it is not possible to lead in the antenna wire, its end can remain outside and be connected to a suitably weatherproofed matching unit. From this a 50Ω length of coaxial cable (any length) can be led round to a suitable entry point, perhaps by a quite circuitous route (Fig 2.11).

An antenna matching unit

Antenna matching units, sometimes called 'antenna tuning units' (ATUs) may be bought in kit form or ready built but they are rather expensive items. Much can be learned about antenna matching by actually making a simple one-band unit. Such a design does not

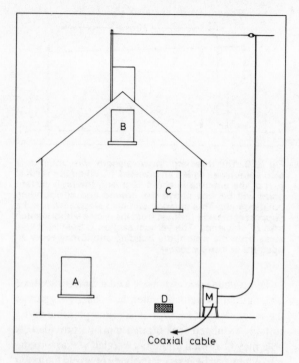

Fig 2.11. When it is not possible to bring the antenna wire directly into the building, an antenna matching unit (M) located in a well-weatherproofed box can be located close to the ground. The 50Ω coaxial feeder to the equipment can then enter the building at any distant point. Windows A, B and C or an airbrick D could be used as entry places

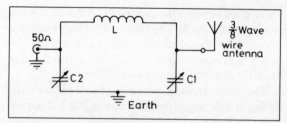

Fig 2.12. The circuit of a 'pi-section' antenna matching unit which will match the impedance of a three-eighth wave wire antenna to a coaxial cable with a 50Ω impedance. The moving plates of the capacitors C1 and C2 must be connected to earth. If a coil former of the dimensions given in the text cannot be obtained, 38 turns of 18SWG enamelled copper wire on a 51mm (2in) former and spaced at six turns per 25mm will work just as well

made of translucent plastic with a diameter of about 76mm (3in) and is ideal. Wash the bottle thoroughly, then cut off the top section, leaving about 14cm (5.5in) from the base. If this improvised coil former can withstand two minutes in a microwave oven (with the obligatory cup of water) without heating or distorting, its RF properties are suitable. Roughen the surface with glass-paper, which will remove advertising material and also give a surface to which the winding will grip more securely and make coil winding easier.

A 5m length of 16SWG enamelled copper wire is needed; this will be more than enough to allow a

involve bandswitching or coil tapping and its circuit is shown in Fig 2.12. This design is well known as a 'pi-section coupler'. It is especially useful in matching a medium impedance antenna to a 50Ω transmitter source or a receiver.

To build this matching unit you will need a pair of variable capacitors. They should each have a maximum capacitance of somewhere between 200 and 350pF. Components of this type are often advertised on the surplus market and they can also be re-cycled from elderly transistor radios. The other chief component is the coil. Small items of hardware such as a coaxial socket, an input terminal and an earth connector are also required, as well as a wooden base and a piece of copper-faced printed circuit board to make a front panel.

The coil is wound on a plastic cylinder and a suitable source for this item can be from a range of domestic bottles used to hold detergents. A particular variety which holds one of the 'ecological' formulations is

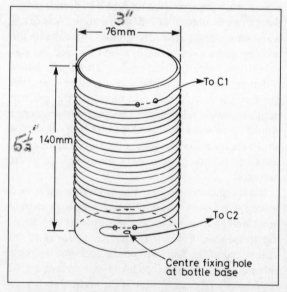

Fig 2.13. Practical coil winding details. When completed it is best to dab some adhesive (such as UHU) at the ends of the winding to hold them securely in place. The wire must be wound on the former very tightly

winding of 20 turns evenly spaced over 10cm (almost 4in). This type of wire is sold by weight and ¼lb should be sufficient.

The coil details are shown in Fig 2.13 and a suitable component layout is shown in Fig 2.14.

The base is a 1cm thick block of plywood (or whatever is to hand) measuring 112 × 120mm and the front panel is a piece of 112 × 152mm circuit board. This is fixed to the base with wood screws and has its copper side inwards, to which the variable capacitors C1 and C2 are fixed. The moving plates of the capacitors must be connected and earthed to the panel face. The fixed plates go to the ends of the coil.

The socket for the PL259 coaxial plug fits on the front panel, as does a terminal for the antenna wire. This terminal must not touch the earthed inner face of the panel. A bolt can be fixed to the panel to act as an earth terminal.

Before this matching unit is used some kind of output indicator will be required. This will show when the unit is correctly tuned and transferring the most energy to the antenna.

Output indicator

As mentioned above, this is needed to help in tuning the antenna matching unit.

The simplest indicator can be a small low-power electric bulb connected in series with the antenna wire and arranged to be shorted across when the tuning procedure is completed (see Fig 2.15). A 6V 60mA bulb is ideal for this purpose and such bulbs are

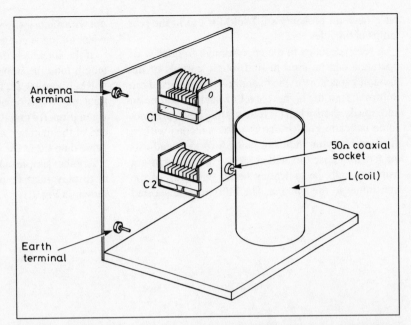

Fig 2.14. A suggested vertical layout for the matching unit components. A horizontal arrangement can also be used but this makes the mounting of the coil more difficult

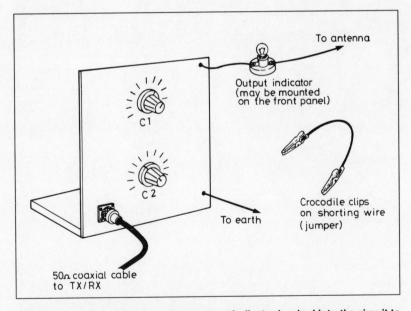

Fig 2.15. How the fuse bulb antenna current indicator is wired into the circuit to help with tuning up. The short 'jumper' wire with 'croc' clips at its ends can be connected across the bulb when tuning is completed

often described in sales catalogues as 'fuse' lamps. Bulbs with the same voltage and current rating were once (and are probably still) sold for use in the rear lamps of bicycles.

A receiver tuned to the approximate frequency of operation can be used to find rough settings of the variable capacitors in the matching unit. Adjust them in turn to find the highest level of background noise and signals, then, when the transmitting key is pressed, some indication of RF output to the antenna will be displayed by your indicator bulb. A further readjustment of the capacitors will usually result in more light from the bulb, so indicating better matching of the transmitter to the antenna. The bulb may be shorted

out with a short wire with a 'crocodile' clip at each end when tuning is completed.

If the antenna is the suggested three-eighths wavelength long, its impedance at the matching unit end will be about 100Ω. The impedance presented by your transmitter will be about 50Ω. You will notice that, when properly tuned, the capacitor C1 at the antenna end of the matcher will be set to a lower capacitance value than C2 at the input end.

Another simple output indicator which uses a meter to display relative power output to the antenna is shown in Fig 7.1.

Chapter 3

Antennas for 10MHz

The Novice frequency allocation within this relatively new amateur band lies between 10.13 and 10.14MHz. The 10MHz or 30m band is one of the WARC (World Amateur Radio Conference) bands, and it was first available to British amateurs in January 1982. The band extends from 10.10 to 10.15MHz and is a shared band, the amateur service being secondary to all other services. There is an unwritten agreement that telephony is never used on the 10MHz band, for this mode might interfere with other band occupants and perhaps even result in its loss to radio amateurs.

Amateur radio contests do not take place on this band, so many amateurs do not invest in beam antennas. Multi-element Yagi beams designed for the band are large structures (each element being about 14m in length) so many of the antennas in use are simple wire structures.

10MHz is very good for daylight short-range communication within Europe (from Britain) and through the winter can be particularly good around mid-day when the 'skip' zone can disappear and contacts be made with stations anywhere out to distances of about 800 miles. Long-distance work is possible during the hours of darkness or at twilight, the limiting factors often being QRM (interference) from non-amateur stations and a rather low level of amateur activity. Signal strengths during daylight hours are usually very good and, when using just 3W power and a dipole antenna, the author has received many reports of signal strength 9 from amateurs on the continent of Europe.

A 10MHz dipole

A half-wave dipole will make an excellent antenna for this band and its dimensions will allow it to be arranged horizontally in a straight line in many locations. When

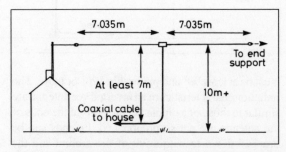

Fig 3.1. A half-wave dipole for 10MHz. The centre insulator may be identical to the one shown in Fig 2.8

cut to be resonant on 10.135MHz (mid Novice band) the dipole will have a top length of 14.07m (46ft 2in) and, if set up at a height of between 10 and 15m, it will be good for long-distance communication as well as shorter 'first skip' distances.

The antenna's centre block and its coaxial connections are as illustrated for the 3.5MHz dipole in Chapter 2. The feeder should drop down vertically from the dipole centre for at least a quarter wavelength (7m or 23ft) before bending round towards the operating position (see Fig 3.1.)

An inverted vee

A conventional horizontal dipole will have some sag at its centre when it is made with wire elements. This lowers the high RF current section of the antenna and reduces its effectiveness as a low-angle radiator for long-distance work. A dipole will also need two end supports. By arranging the dipole as an 'inverted vee' (Fig 3.2), just one support is needed and the high-current centre section will be well elevated. An additional bonus is that the antenna will fit into a smaller plot.

The angle of the vee between the legs of the dipole

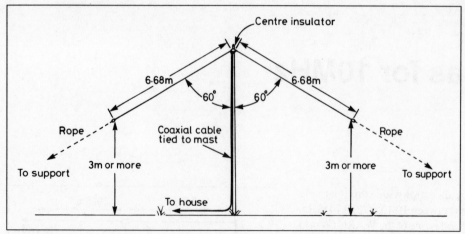

Fig 3.2. Practical arrangements for an inverted vee antenna designed for the 10MHz band

must be at least 90° and preferably 120° or more. The radiation characteristics of an inverted vee antenna are similar to those of a dipole but the nulls at the ends of the antenna are not so pronounced. Its ends can be dropped down to within 3m of the ground and the antenna will present a good match to a 50Ω impedance coaxial feeder. Dropping the dipole legs towards the ground results in a lowering of its resonant frequency so it must be made about 5% shorter than a normal horizontal dipole. The total length of the top when used on the 10MHz band as an inverted vee must be 13.36m (43ft 10in).

A balun for the dipole and the inverted vee

A dipole is a balanced antenna but a coaxial feeder is unbalanced and its outer braid conductor is within the RF field of the radiating antenna top. This imbalance does not greatly affect the working of the dipole but it can give rise to radiation from the coaxial braid and upset the expected radiation pattern of the antenna. It will also increase the probability of television break-through or interference (TVI). This feeder radiation will be vertically polarised and the imbalance will also produce a distorted or 'squinting' radiation pattern.

These problems can be corrected if a device called a 'balun' (short for 'balanced to unbalanced') is used. There are several types of balun but perhaps the simplest is an RF choke made with the coaxial feeder close to its connection with the dipole centre.

An RF choke is a coil (inductor) with enough inductance to prevent RF from the antenna travelling

down on the outside of the feeder braid. In order to reduce the number of turns needed (and reduce weight) a ferrite ring can be used to increase inductance (see Fig 3.3).

Five turns of coaxial cable wound as a 150mm diameter coil, together with a pair of ferrite rings, will make a balun for 10MHz. Suitable ferrite rings can be obtained from the RSGB or Ferromagnetics of Mold in North Wales (see Appendix 1), and they are usually purchased to clear RF breakthrough problems on the connecting cables of domestic hi-fi equipment or

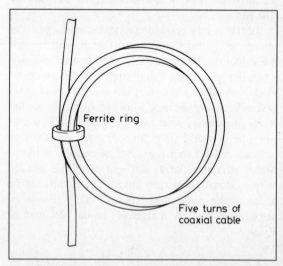

Fig 3.3. A five-turn balun made with the dipole coaxial feeder and a ferrite ring to increase its inductance. A pair of rings cemented together will make a more effective balun. The coaxial cable is held in position by binding it with insulating tape or tying it with a nylon or similar cord. The ferrite ring is also tied to the coaxial coil

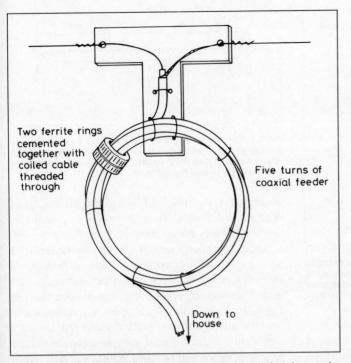

Fig 3.4. The considerable weight of the coiled cable is taken up by tying it to the centre insulator block

The radio amateur must try to make a low-resistance earth system if the use of a Marconi antenna is contemplated. Earth resistance varies from place to place and from time to time through the seasons, and on chalky downland or very sandy areas it is high at all times. Even in a domestic garden the soil resistance can vary greatly within distances of a few metres.

The minimum earthing requirement for an amateur Marconi antenna would be a stout copper or aluminium rod driven 2m into the ground. By using more than one rod the earth resistance can be lowered considerably (Fig 3.6) but the addition of a 'counterpoise' wire or wires can greatly improve the efficiency of Marconi antennas even in places where the ground resistance is inherently high.

A counterpoise is a wire which is at least a quarter of a wavelength long, and which is run out above the ground, lying on the surface or buried for just a few centimetres (Fig 3.7). The ground system

telephones etc. The rings have an internal 'hole' with a diameter of 25mm which is more than enough to take the five turns of coaxial cable which make up the balun coil. If two rings, cemented together ('super glue' is suitable for this, but take care when using this substance) are used they are then tied to the balun coil with a thin nylon or similar cord. This cord is also used to secure the balun to the dipole centre insulator (Fig 3.4).

There are other balun types that would be suitable for connecting coaxial cable to balanced antennas and two will be described in later chapters.

A Marconi antenna

At the start of the present century Marconi had already realised that the earth could replace one half of his antenna systems, and antennas based upon this principle are known as 'Marconi antennas' (Fig 3.5). Unfortunately the earth is not a very good electrical conductor and, unless a Marconi antenna is surrounded by salt water or is located on a salt marsh, the ground resistance will greatly reduce its efficiency.

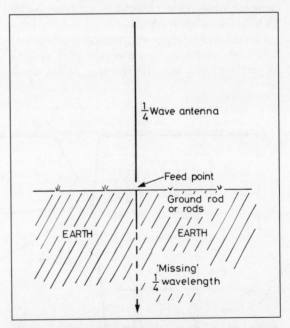

Fig 3.5. A basic Marconi antenna where the missing quarter-wave of a dipole system is replaced by the earth. Unless the earth is very conductive a quarter-wave Marconi antenna will be very inefficient

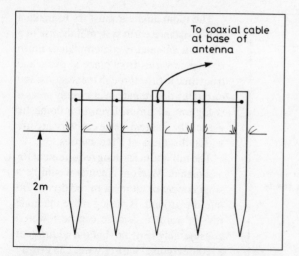

Fig 3.6. How several earth rods may be inter-connected to reduce the earth resistance in a Marconi antenna system. It is often easier and cheaper to arrange for counterpoise wires or buried earth wires when planning a Marconi antenna

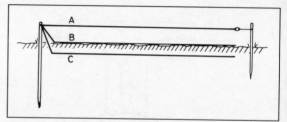

Fig 3.7. Three earthing arrangements. (a) A counterpoise wire or group of wires positioned above the ground. (b) A wire or wires lying on the surface. (c) Wires buried a few centimetres below the surface

will be much more effective if more than one wire is used. Any additional counterpoise wires should run out in different directions and not lie close together (Fig 3.8). A basic quarter-wave Marconi antenna using an earthing rod and additional counterpoise wire (or wires) is shown in Fig 3.9.

Unfortunately a single-wire Marconi antenna has a base feed impedance in the region of 5 to 20Ω (depending upon the effectiveness of the earth arrangements) and this is difficult to match to a standard 50Ω coaxial feeder. There are ways to match this antenna but they are not recommended to the Novice.

Should the single wire of the Marconi be replaced by a pair of closely spaced parallel wires that are shorted together at the far end of the antenna, a feed impedance step-up of four times can be achieved (see Fig 3.10). If this double quarter-wave arrangement is set up vertically or near vertically and fed against a single earth rod and at least one counterpoise wire, its feed impedance will be close to 48Ω and will match well into a 50Ω coaxial cable. This antenna's efficiency will also be raised to about 40%.

This can go up to as much as 70% when a very good earth system is used. The parallel antenna wires have a total length of 7m (23ft) and are made from a length of 300Ω ribbon feeder. The slotted 'Bofa' variety is the best for it is little affected by damp weather

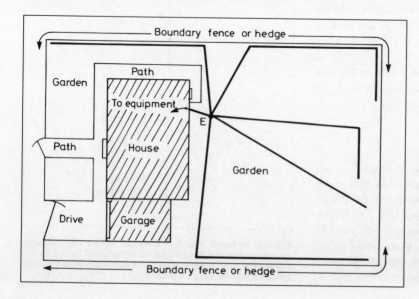

Fig 3.8. Plan view of a typical earth wire or counterpoise system arranged in a small garden. The wires along the boundary may be inside a hedge or fixed to a fence. The buried wires can be positioned to avoid features such as ponds, sheds, greenhouses or permanent garden plots. All the wires are connected to an earth rod E close to the house. A thick conductor wire which can be several thinner wires in parallel should be used to connect between the earth rod and the equipment

Fig 3.9. A practical Marconi antenna where the quarter-wave radiator M is a single wire arranged to be vertical or almost vertical. F is the feed point where the coaxial feeder connects to the base of M and the earth rod E. The counterpoise wires A and B join to the earth rod as does the buried wire C. Unfortunately a single-wire Marconi antenna of this type has a very low feed impedance and would not match a 50Ω feeder

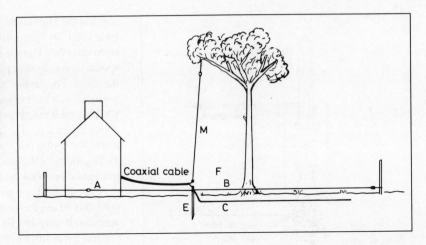

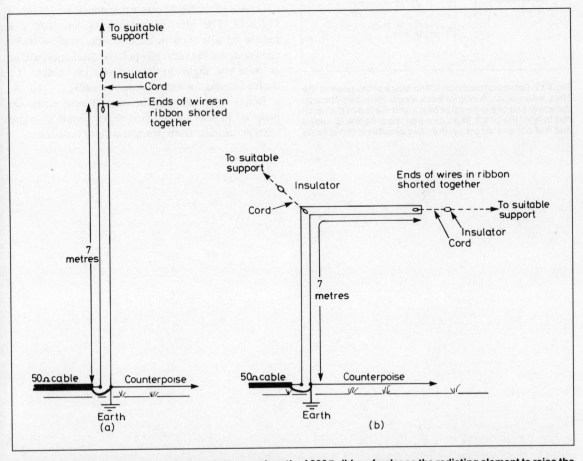

Fig 3.10. (a) A Marconi antenna using a quarter-wavelength of 300Ω ribbon feeder as the radiating element to raise the feed impedance by a factor of four which allows a reasonable match to a 50Ω impedance coaxial feeder. (b) When it is not possible to arrange for the 7m radiator to be completely vertical it may slope or run away at right angles for part of its length. The vertical section must be kept as long as is practicable and must not be shorter than 50% of the complete length

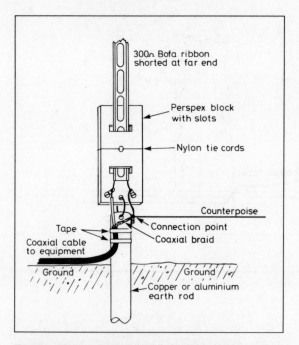

300Ω Bofa ribbon
shorted at far end

Perspex block
with slots

Nylon tie cords

Counterpoise

Connection point

Tape

Coaxial braid

Coaxial cable
to equipment

Ground

Ground

Copper or aluminium
earth rod

Fig 3.11. Details of the connection block at the base of the Marconi antenna. A loop of thick wire is threaded through the lower end of the perspex block and the top of the earth rod to hold the block in place when the antenna is raised and not put any strain on the coaxial cable connections

conditions. The counterpoise wire or wires should also be at least 7m long and they can be buried to be out of sight after first cutting slots with the business end of a spade. Grass or other plants will soon grow again over the slots. The author has successfully used counterpoise wires which ran along wooden fences and some which were located inside boundary hedges about 1m above the ground. The actual disposal of, and arrangements for laying out, counterpoise wires can be left to the ingenuity of the reader for much will depend upon individual property and garden layouts.

A small insulator and a length of nylon or similar cord may be used to hold up the far end of the Marconi antenna. It may not be possible to have the antenna vertical for its full length and a part or all of the antenna can slope from the vertical (Fig 3.10).

Details of the feed-point arrangement are shown in Fig 3.11. The Marconi antenna as described will radiate equally well in all directions (unless badly screened) and the vertically polarised radiation will be at quite low angles to the horizon. This makes it a useful antenna for long distance working.

Before antenna wires or counterpoise wires are installed in your garden first make certain that you have permission from parents, wife or husband!

Chapter 4

Antennas for 21 and 28MHz

British Novices are fortunate in having frequency allocations within the 21 and 28MHz bands, for these bands can be used for medium- and long-distance communication even with low transmitter powers and simple antennas. Novices in the USA also have frequencies on these bands which partly coincide with the British Novice frequencies.

The 21MHz band is normally open through the hours of daylight, although in the summer months conditions often allow long-distance contacts well after nightfall and occasionally right through until sunrise.

Similarly, long-distance propagation on 28MHz is also usually restricted to the hours of daylight but the band is also greatly affected by solar activity. During the years of minimum sunspot activity, the 28MHz band is often closed for long periods and only short-range contacts are then possible.

In the summer months during daylight hours the 28MHz band enjoys a phenomenon which is called 'ES' or 'Sporadic E' propagation, and which permits good strong signals between stations in Europe and just beyond. As its name implies, this mode of propagation cannot be relied upon on a daily basis but between early summer and the autumn there are many days when a few watts of power will allow contacts with stations between 200 and 1,500 miles away. At or close to the peak of a solar cycle maximum (an event which happens approximately every 11 years), the 28MHz band can 'open' for really long-distance work and low-powered stations are then able to have world-wide contacts with amateurs all over the six continents.

The 28MHz band is always useful for semi-local communication by ground-wave propagation which may take place at any time of day or night and at any season or year. This makes the band a favourite with many local groups or 'nets'. There is not the high level of noise or interference that is found on the lower-frequency HF bands, and power levels of a few watts are sufficient for reliable contacts. The ranges on ground-wave propagation will be similar to those achieved by CB operators on the adjacent 27MHz band, and may extend to 20 miles or more when operating from a good elevated site.

Half-wave dipoles for 21 and 28MHz

Wire dipoles for these bands can usually be erected in small or average-sized gardens, and when they are between 7 and 10m above the ground they will give excellent results.

If an outside antenna cannot possibly be put up, a dipole for either of the bands can be situated in the loft or roof space of a house. If this is done it will not be such an effective antenna and there may be the risk of EMC (electromagnetic compatibility) problems on domestic TV and audio or recording apparatus. A poorly sited outside antenna is always better than one located indoors where there are so many wires, pipes and other objects which will screen or detune it.

A half-wave dipole will show some directivity and will be best for transmitting and receiving in the directions at right angles to the run of the antenna. Full world coverage can be achieved if two dipoles are put up and arranged to be at right angles to each other. The two antennas can be spaced well apart and a simple switching arrangement can be arranged so that there is a rapid choice of dipole. A cheap 'knife switch' (see Fig 4.1) can be used to switch the coaxial feeders.

On the higher-frequency bands such as 21 and 28MHz a half-wave dipole becomes much shorter in length, so, when it is made up, measuring the wire length becomes more critical. Some allowance must

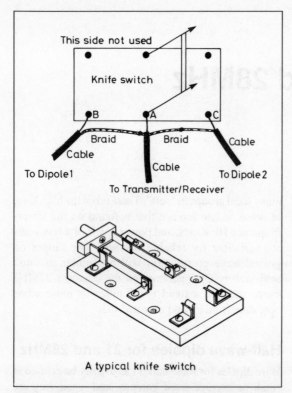

Fig 4.1. How to wire up a knife switch so that either of two dipole antennas can be selected. The braids on the three coaxial cables are soldered together and do not have to be switched

be made for the loops through the end and centre insulators (Fig 4.2). The correct lengths of each leg of a dipole cut for either the 21 or 28MHz band are also given in Fig 4.2.

The balun illustrated in Fig 3.4 of Chapter 3 can be scaled down for use on 21 or 28MHz and the diameter of the coiled coaxial cable will then be 90mm (3.5in). A balun is not essential but it will lessen any chance of radiation from the feeder and will also ensure that the dipole radiates properly with maximum radiation at right angles to the wire top.

Where space is restricted the dipole can slope down from one high point and a slope angle of not more than 45° from the horizontal is best. This will change the radiation pattern of the antenna and the radiation will tend to be towards the low end of the wire, although there will still be some radiation from the sides.

When a sloping dipole is used its feeder must still come away from the centre at right angles for at least a quarter-wavelength (that is the same length as one

leg of the dipole). Dipoles for 21 and 28MHz can have insulators and centre connecting blocks similar to those described for the 3.5 and 10MHz bands in earlier chapters.

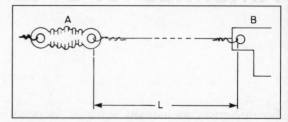

Fig 4.2. The length L represents each leg of a dipole. L is 2.53m long (8ft 3in) when the antenna is designed for 28MHz and 3.38m long (11ft 1in) for 21MHz. The measurements become more critical on the higher-frequency bands and the end loops at the insulators A and B must be allowed for

Vertical antennas for 21 and 28MHz

A vertical antenna radiates vertically polarised energy and this leaves the antenna towards all points of the compass. The angle of maximum radiation in relation to the horizon will be low, which makes it very effective for both long-distance sky-wave work and semi-local contacts using the ground wave.

Many designs for vertical antennas on the amateur bands use vertical metal tubes or rods a quarter of a wavelength long, and also several horizontal rods or wires which are also a quarter of a wavelength long. Antennas made this way are often called 'ground planes' for they are similar to the basic Marconi antenna but use the horizontal conductors as an artificial earth or 'ground plane'.

When a half-wave dipole is arranged as shown in Fig 4.3, with its lower leg horizontal, it will radiate both vertically and horizontally polarised RF energy. If a second additional lower leg is connected so that it runs out horizontally away from the first, the RF currents in the two horizontal wires will cancel and leave just the vertical wire to radiate (see Fig 4.4).

This arrangement makes an effective antenna but has the drawback that its feed impedance is only about 30Ω and will not match standard 50Ω coaxial cable. If the two horizontal wires are sloped down at an angle of 40° from the horizontal, the feed-point impedance is raised to 50Ω and a good match to the coaxial cable is possible (see Fig 4.5).

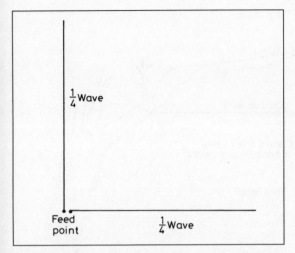

Fig 4.3. A half-wave dipole with one vertical and one horizontal leg

A useful antenna design for either the 21 or 28MHz bands can be based upon the arrangement shown in Fig 4.5, and it can be made easily and cheaply with wire. It is suggested that 16 or 18SWG copper wire is used to make this antenna and also that there is no need to have a mast or similar vertical support.

The vertical wire can be supported by being tied to a piece of fishing line (a heavy-gauge, mono-filament nylon type) which can go up to any convenient overhead point. A tree branch or a horizontal cord will serve to hold up the vertical wire. No insulator is needed because the nylon line is itself a fine insulator and will not absorb moisture.

The sloping wires must have small insulators at

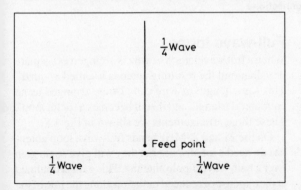

Fig 4.4. When two quarter-wave wires are horizontal and in line as shown, the horizontally polarised radiation will largely cancel out and leave a vertically polarised signal from the vertical quarter-wave

their ends and then can be correctly positioned by cords which come down to suitable anchor points on the ground. To get the correct 40° slope downwards it is only necessary to arrange that the ends of these wires are 5.2m (17ft) apart on a 21MHz antenna or 4m (13ft 2in) apart on a 28MHz version.

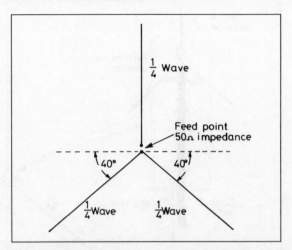

Fig 4.5. If the two horizontal wires slope down at angles of 40° from the horizontal, the impedance at the feed point will then match a standard 50Ω coaxial cable

The coaxial feeder will come down below the vertical wire and its weight will stabilise that wire, which will also be held firm by a line dropping to the ground from the connection insulator. The feeder can run back to the house along the ground or be buried a few centimetres. Design details of this antenna are shown in Fig 4.6.

An 'upside down' version of this antenna can be made, and the author has experimented successfully with several of these. The inverted top-fed quarter-wave vertical is particularly useful when the shack or operating room is located at the top of a house. The maximum radiation will take place from the high-current section of the wire where the feeder connects and which will be well elevated.

The lower end of the vertical wire may be held down with a thin nylon cord tied to a ground stake or instead have a weight system of a double pendulum to prevent too much sway. The author has used a lead fishing weight in combination with a solid hard rubber 'dog ball' in this way and the antenna only swung wildly in really strong winds. The lower weight (the ball) was

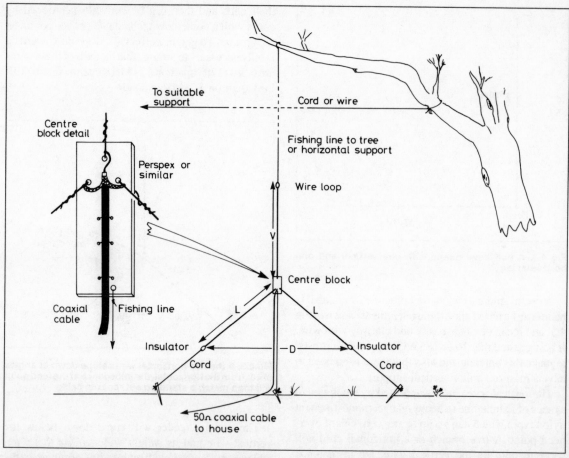

Fig 4.6. A practical vertical antenna which may be suspended from a convenient overhead tie point. If made for the 21MHz band the lengths of V and L will be 3.38m (11ft 1in) and the distance between the ends of the sloping wires D will be 5.2m (17ft). On 28MHz V and L will be 2.53m (8ft 3in) and D will be 4m (13ft 2in). The lower ends of the sloping wires can come down to within a metre of the ground but the antenna will be more effective if it is higher. The centre block is shown in detail and may be a piece of perspex or similar plastic material. All the connections must be soldered and well-weatherproofed. A generous application of a silicone rubber sealant will keep out moisture. The coaxial cable is tied to the block to take any strain from the soldered connections

high enough not to be bumped into even by a very tall person!

Practical details of an inverted vertical antenna for either band are shown in Fig 4.7. The coaxial feeder must on no account lie below its connection point and should run back to the house or operating position at right angles to the top section for at least a quarter-wavelength (that is, the length of half the top horizontal wire). The weight of the vertical wire and any attachments will pull down the top wires so that they slope. They can be given the same slope angle of 40° as in the earlier (Fig 4.6) version of the antenna, ensuring a proper match to the 50Ω coaxial feeder.

Full-wave loops

When a full wavelength of wire is arranged as a square or a diamond the resulting antenna is called a 'quad'. This same length of wire can also be arranged as an equilateral triangle and then it becomes a 'delta loop'. These three arrangements are shown in Fig 4.8.

On the 21 and 28MHz bands full-wave loop antennas do need a lot of space but they will give some gain over a half-wave dipole antenna. This gain is obtained at the expense of reduced radiation along the line of the horizontal wires or wire of the system. When you look through the loop from either side you are looking in the two directions of maximum radiation.

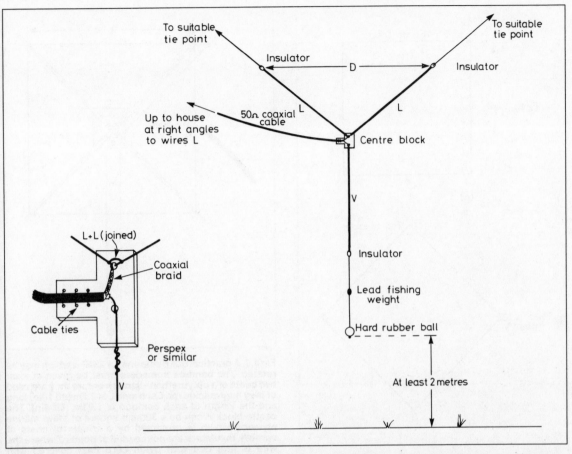

Fig 4.7. An inverted quarter-wave vertical antenna. The dimensions V, L and D are as described in Fig 4.6. The centre block is 'T' shaped and the usual precautions against strain and dampness must be taken. The lower end of the wire V can be held down with a length of nylon cord but when the antenna height is sufficient a 'pendulum' may be used. The two lengths of cord in this arrangement must not be equal in length. When of differing lengths the natural 'periods' or swing times of each pendulum will counteract and help to stabilise the antenna

A 28MHz quad loop can be mounted on bamboo spreaders (Fig 4.9) and then it can be rotated. A turn of 180° is enough to cover all directions. Quads for 21 and 28MHz can be fixed to a pair of elevated tie points and suitably anchored at their bases. If the triangular 'delta' design is used just a single centre support (non-metallic) will be needed (Fig 4.10).

Full-wave loops cannot be fed directly with 50Ω impedance coaxial cables for they have a feed impedance lying between 100 and 120Ω. There is a 95Ω coaxial cable which is now available (type PG62A) which can be connected directly to a loop antenna. This will be a fair match to the antenna but an ATU or matching unit will be needed to bring the impedance down to the nominal 50Ω required by most transmitters.

A suitable ATU (also known as an 'AMU') is described later in this chapter.

To allow direct connection of the feeder to the transmitter, a matching transformer can be made by using two different types of coaxial cable. Such a transformer uses a short length of 75Ω impedance coaxial between the antenna feed point and the main 50Ω feeder. The length of this 75Ω section is critical for each frequency band and details are given in Fig 4.11. Suitable 75Ω coaxial is the type used for domestic TV antennas.

Loop antennas do not have to be so high as dipoles. Their lower wires need only be 2 or 3m above the ground, just high enough to allow one to walk beneath them. The loops described and shown in the illustrations

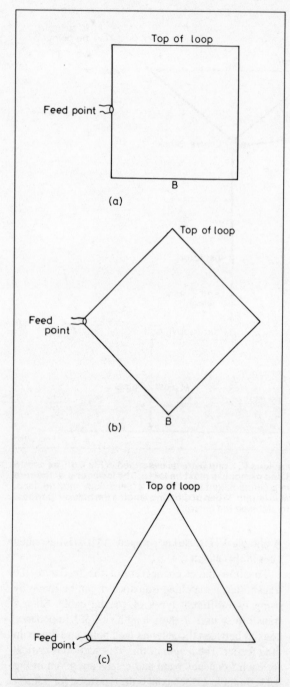

Fig 4.8. Three full-wave loop antennas: (a) a square quad; (b) a diamond quad; (c) a delta loop. The lower section of each is marked B and when the feed points shown are used the radiated signals will be vertically polarised. The quad sides will each be 3.6m (11ft 10in) for 21MHz and 2.7m (8ft 10in) for 28MHz. The delta loop sides will be 4.83m (15ft 10in) for 21MHz and 3.6m (11ft 10in) for 28MHz

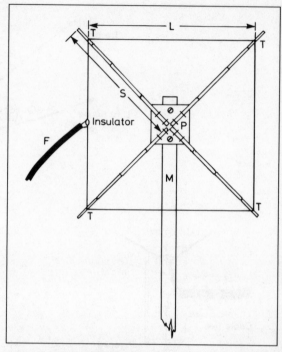

Fig 4.9. A practical quad antenna for 28MHz which may be rotated. The bamboo spreaders must be given at least two coats of a polyurethane varnish before they are used or they may quickly rot. Each side L is 2.7m (8ft 10in) long and the length of each bamboo is 1.93m (6ft 4in). The centre block P can be a 300mm square of stout marine plywood which is protected by a couple of coats of varnish. Insulators are not needed at points T where the wire is first tied with nylon cord then covered with insulating tape. The bamboos are fixed to the centre board with small U bolts. The mast M may be any convenient length of timber bolted to the centre block and long enough to keep the lower wire of the antenna at least 2m from the ground. The feeder F is part of a coaxial transformer (see Fig 4.11) so a good match can be made to the impedance at the feed point

are vertically polarised and will provide the low angles of radiation needed for long-distance contacts. They will generally out-perform any dipole at the same height.

End-fed wire antennas

Just about the simplest antenna is an end-fed wire. Any length or wire can be used as an antenna if it is matched to the transmitter or receiver. Unfortunately the impedance at the transmitter (feed) end of a single wire can range from just a few ohms to a thousand ohms or more. This impedance depends upon the length of the antenna and also the frequency being used.

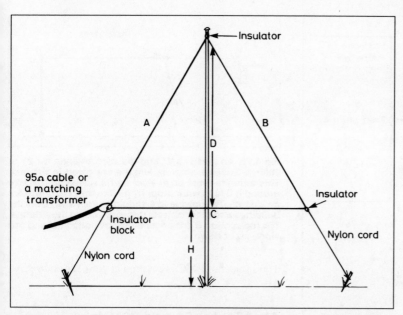

Fig 4.10. A delta loop antenna for 21 or 28MHz. Each side A, B and C is the same length and measurements for each band are given in Fig 4.8. Insulators are needed at each corner and the support mast should be non-metallic. The length D will be 4.2m (13ft 10in) when the antenna is cut for 21MHz and 3.1m (10ft 2in) for 28MHz. Suitable minimum mast lengths for the lower section H are 4m and 3m for the 21 and 28MHz bands respectively. The wire C must not rub against the mast

Fortunately a matching unit or ATU can be used to give correct matching but it is best to use a wire length that does not present a very high or very low impedance to the ATU, for even a well-made unit will not work well at the two extreme impedance values. Many commercially made ATUs cannot match wires that have a feed impedance of more than 500Ω!

The far end of every end-fed wire, regardless of length, will have a very high impedance value and it is by 'working forward' from the far end that the impedance at the near ends of wires can be deduced.

There are few rules about the placing of an end-fed wire antenna but it must obviously not be close to buildings or trees and it must be as high as possible. The run of the wire need not be straight and bends can be made when the available space is limited or awkwardly shaped. A good insulator must be used at the far end where the impedance is high.

Perhaps the simplest arrangement is the popular 'inverted L' (Fig 4.12). This will give good results all round, for the vertical section fills the radiation pattern gaps of the horizontal top. It is best to slope the vertical section away from a house wall to keep the wire in the

clear. Upstairs operating positions can have the wire running out almost horizontally for its entire length.

A low-loss entry hole is needed and the body of an empty plastic ballpoint pen in a hole drilled through a wooden window frame will be effective. Do not have the entry point well away from the operating position, for this will mean that quite a long run of the antenna will be in the house.

End-fed wires work better when they operate against a counterpoise wire, which is a quarter-wavelength of wire connected to the earth terminal of the ATU. It can be dropped outside to hang below the window, run around the floor under carpets etc, or be taped to a wall or skirting board. Two will be required if work on both 21 and 28MHz is contemplated. The counterpoise length is equal to the length of half of or one leg of a dipole antenna.

End-fed wire lengths to avoid are multiples of a quarter-wavelength and the following lengths should work well with most ATUs:

28MHz: 6.3m (20ft 7in), 8.8m (28ft 11in), 11.3m (37ft), 13.8m (45ft 5in)
21MHz: 8.4m (27ft 8in), 11.8m (38ft 9in), 15.2m (49ft 10in)

It is obvious that wire lengths of about 8.6m and 11.5m would be effective on both bands. The suggested lengths are not critical and may be adjusted to plus or minus about 300mm (1ft).

Although easy to set up, end-fed wires can create problems. They have RF energy all along their lengths and, where the antenna wire is close to or actually inside a building, it may bring about EMC difficulties.

This could lead to 'breakthrough' on your own or a neighbour's TV set (TVI), video recorder or audio equipment (including telephones). This breakthrough is usually a result of poor design or a fault in the

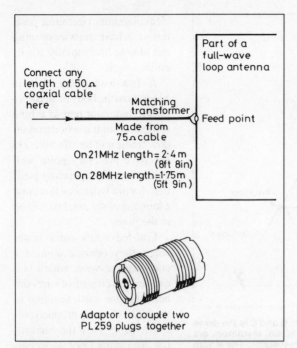

Connect any length of 50Ω coaxial cable here

Part of a full-wave loop antenna

Matching transformer

Feed point

Made from 75Ω cable

On 21MHz length = 2·4 m (8ft 8in)

On 28MHz length = 1·75 m (5ft 9in)

Adaptor to couple two PL259 plugs together

Fig 4.11. Quarter-wave transformers made with lengths of 75Ω coaxial cable can be used to match a 50Ω feeder to the loops. Where the 75Ω section and the 50Ω coaxial cable are joined, standard PL259 plugs and a suitable adaptor should be used. The plugs and the adaptor should be weatherproofed. At the loop antenna feed points small perspex blocks can be used (see Fig 4.7), silicone rubber or similar weatherproofing being applied

apparatus suffering the breakthrough – it cannot reject signals that it was not designed to receive or pick up.

Antennas fed with coaxial cable can be located some distance away from one's own or neighbouring properties but end-fed wire antennas must necessarily enter your property.

It is unlikely that many transmissions using power levels of 3W will cause EMC problems but it could happen when a particular TV set or other domestic apparatus is badly designed or severely out of order.

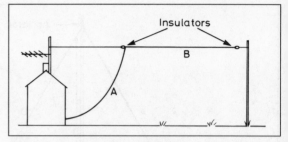

Insulators

Fig 4.12. An inverted 'L' end-fed wire antenna for 21 or 28MHz. Suitable antenna lengths are given in the text. This antenna must be at least half a wavelength above ground if it is to work properly (6.75m on 21MHz and 5m on 28MHz). The downlead A should be kept away from the buildings and other objects that may screen the antenna. The top section B does not have to be horizontal and can slope up or down

The subject of EMC is covered in your Worksheet No 31.

An ATU for 21 and 28MHz

The ATU described in Chapter 2 and shown in Fig 2.12 can be modified to work on 21 and 28MHz.

The coil L should be replaced with a new air-wound coil made with 16SWG enamelled copper wire, having four complete turns with an inside diameter of 35mm (1³⁄₈in) and pulled out to a length of 30mm (¾in). When making the coil, find a cylinder with a diameter a little less than the inside diameter needed, for the wire will 'spring' after it is wound and removed. Small pill or tablet containers or other domestic plastic containers abound in many sizes and diameters.

The capacitors C1 and C2 may be retained but instead new components can be used. C1 requires a maximum capacitance of 150pF and C2 should be a 300pF maximum variable capacitor.

Both capacitors should be adjusted until a maximum RF current on the antenna wire is achieved. This is a simple way to tune up and it is better to employ an SWR meter (see Chapter 7).

Chapter 5

Antennas for 1.9MHz

British Class A licence holders may operate on the 1.81 to 2MHz band. This is often called 'Top Band' for it is the highest waveband in metres (about 160m) allocated to amateurs. The Novice is only allowed to operate within part of this band, between 1.95 and 2MHz on a wavelength of approximately 150m.

Low power and average-sized antennas on this frequency band limit the normal communication range to several hundreds of miles, these distances only being possible during the hours of darkness. At certain times, especially around sunrise and sunset when conditions are ideal, it is possible to contact stations thousands of miles away, but this can only be achieved when stations are equipped with excellent antenna systems.

Ground-wave propagation is good on 1.9MHz which makes it ideal for local and semi-local contacts. Many radio clubs and groups have 'round tables' or 'nets' on the band. With low power and simple antennas a range of 20 to 30 miles is possible at any time. After nightfall, especially through the winter months, it is possible to make contact with stations beyond the ground-wave range, and when conditions are suitable with stations all over Europe. Unfortunately the Novice frequencies are not normally used for contacts with stations outside Britain but there are many local nets and individual operators working between 1.95 and 2MHz.

Some amateurs still use AM (amplitude modulation) telephony, and transmitters which work in this mode are simple and easy to construct.

A 1.9MHz dipole

A half-wave dipole for this band will have a top length of 72.4m (237ft). Not many amateurs in urban areas can put up such a long antenna and additionally it must be at least a quarter-wavelength above the ground if it is to work at all reasonably. This means a minimum height of 36m (about 118ft).

The radiation from a horizontal dipole has little ground wave and will not be an effective antenna for semi-local working; not so good in fact as a much shorter length of wire arranged as a Marconi antenna.

Series-tuned wire antennas

By using an ATU, almost any length of elevated wire can be used as a Marconi antenna and matched to the needed 50Ω equipment impedance. The ATU system shown in Fig 5.1 will tune wire antennas ranging in length from about 12m (40ft) to 30m (100ft). The end-fed antennas suggested for the 3.5 and 21MHz bands (see Figs 2.10 and 4.12) will be effective on 1.9MHz, especially if they are arranged as inverted 'L's.

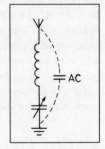

Fig 5.1. A series-tuned ATU where AC represents the antenna's capacitance to ground which is in series with the rest of the circuit. This arrangement is useful when the antenna is shorter than a quarter-wavelength. A practical example of this arrangement is shown in Fig 5.3

A better ground wave is radiated if much of the wire is vertical. The wire does not have to be in a straight line and so long as it is kept away from walls and other screening objects it can be bent about to fit into the available space. When the garden length is very limited a few metres of the far end of the antenna can be folded as shown in Fig 5.2. Folding in this way will not

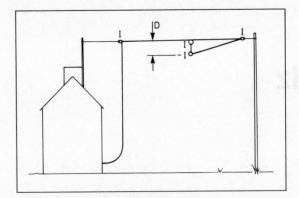

Fig 5.2. When the garden length is restricted, the far end of an inverted 'L' antenna can be bent back as shown. The insulators are marked I and the distance between the horizontal top and the end of the wire (D) should be about 1m. A nylon cord separates the two insulators at D

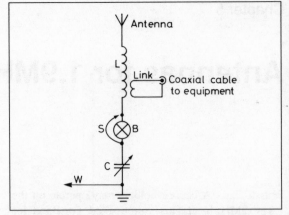

Fig 5.3. The complete practical circuit for the 1.9MHz ATU. Details of the coil L and the link winding are given in Fig 5.4. The variable capacitor C is a 500pF component and suitable examples are found in old broadcast receivers. They may still be obtained as new items but can be quite expensive. The wire W represents one or more counterpoise wires. They may be buried, laid on the ground or elevated as described in Chapter 3. The wire S is used to short out the bulb when tuning up is completed. If counterpoise wires cannot be used a good earth connection is needed

have a great effect upon the antenna performance for most of the radiation is off the wire nearest the operating position.

The dipoles suggested for the 3.5 and 10MHz bands may be used as top-loaded Marconi antennas. This is done by joining together the coaxial braid and the inner conductor at the equipment end and connecting them to the ATU. A dipole cannot be used like this when the feeder is buried or lying on the ground for the feeder is the actual radiating part of the antenna when 'strapped' in this manner.

Marconi antennas need a good, low-resistance earth connection if they are to be effective. The efficiency of a short antenna as described will rise dramatically as the earthing system is improved. A connection to an outside cold water pipe will provide a fair earth but as plastic replaces metal for water pipes this kind of earth will soon no longer be available. Several earth rods (see Fig 3.6) together with buried wires or a counterpoise arrangement as shown in Fig 3.8 will give a good earth system for short Marconi antennas.

A series-tuned ATU for 1.9MHz

The circuit for this ATU is shown in Fig 5.3. The antenna is connected to the loading coil L, the other end of which goes to earth via a variable capacitor C. The antenna, the coil, the capacitor and the ground make a series-tuned circuit which can be adjusted to be resonant at the operating frequency.

The connection to the equipment is made using a small coil called a 'link' winding, coupled to and at the 'earthy' end of L. This winding connects to the equipment through a short length of 50Ω coaxial cable.

A small lamp bulb is shown in the earth lead. This is a tuning indicator and it will shine brightest when the antenna system is tuned to the transmitter frequency. A 1 or 2W bulb is suitable. The author discovered that, when using a variety of antenna lengths, a 0.36W fuse bulb could be lit brilliantly when only 0.5W output power was used.

The bulb has resistance and takes power, so when tuning up is finished it should be taken out of the circuit. This can be done easily by shorting it across with an inch or so of wire. A wire with a 'crocodile' clip at one end will be effective.

The details of the coil L and the link winding are shown in Fig 5.4. Practical arrangements such as layout of the ATU components are shown in Fig 5.5.

An indoor antenna for 1.9MHz

A member of my local AM net which operates on 1.950MHz each weekend has his equipment in an upstairs room. He used a 12m horizontal wire which ran out to a pole at the end of his short garden as a

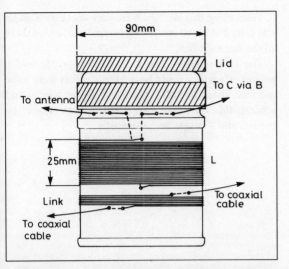

Fig 5.4. The coil L can be wound on a disused plastic dried milk container. Its main winding has 30 turns of 20SWG enamelled copper wire closely wound over 25mm. Before winding the coil it is best to roughen the container surface with glass-paper. The ends of the winding are secured by making 'stitches' as shown. The link winding is put just below the main coil and has four turns of plastic-covered 'hook-up' wire. The 30 turn winding will require 9m (30ft) of wire and a quarter of a pound of wire will provide this length. The link winding needs about 1.5m (5ft) of wire. A single wood screw will hold the coil former down to the ATU baseboard

Marconi antenna but found that his signals were weak at distances of five miles or more. Some members of

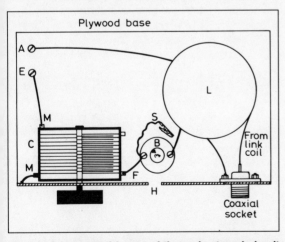

Fig 5.5. A suggested layout of the series-tuned circuit ATU. The front panel can be a piece of copper-faced circuit board and the hole in this (marked H) is made in front of where the bulb will be placed. The connections M on the variable capacitor are to the moving plates and F goes to the fixed plates. A and E are the antenna and earth terminals

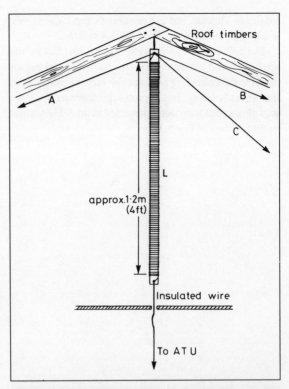

Fig 5.6. Details of the indoor vertical antenna for 1.9MHz. The long coil is suspended on a short piece of cord or string and the wires A, B and C are soldered to the top of the coil winding. These wires are not cut to any critical length but each should preferably be at least 3m (10ft) long. They must not come down vertically but run out either horizontally or slope down at a small angle. The insulated wire below the coil leads down to the ATU and can be of any convenient length. No insulators are needed at the ends of the top loading wires for they are indoors in a dry environment

the group had great difficulty in copying him through the background noise (man-made mostly) which is so often found on this band.

Fortunately he had a large roof space or loft which could accommodate a short vertical loaded antenna as designed by the author. This antenna is shown in Fig 5.6. The loading coil L was wound with about 57m (190ft) of PVC-insulated 'bell wire' along a 21mm diameter plastic tube. The tube is usually white and sold in DIY shops as 'plumber's waste pipe', coming in 2m lengths. The winding will take up just under 1.2m (4ft) of tube and will have about 800 turns.

Three 6m (20ft) wires connect to the 'top' of the coil and run out to convenient tie points in the roof space. These wires are not critical in length; they may be longer or shorter, but are needed as top-capacitance loading of the system. They do not radiate.

The coil is tied to the highest point just below the roof ridge and a wire soldered to its lower end passes down to the operating position through a small hole in the 'shack' ceiling. In the prototype antenna this wire was almost 6m long and connected to an ATU similar to that shown in Fig 5.3.

Tests using this antenna were very successful and it was possible to put out strong ground-wave signals to all the net members.

The coil winding had a resistance of 5Ω and a greater efficiency could be achieved if this were to be reduced. Using 18SWG enamelled copper wire would achieve this but more than 1¼lb of wire would be needed and it might be quite costly.

Chapter 6

Antennas for 50 and 434MHz

The 50 and 434MHz bands are VHF and UHF (very high frequency and ultra high frequency) bands and have propagation characteristics that are quite different from those shown on the HF bands.

The 50MHz band, which is also known as the '6m band', has only been available to radio amateurs in Europe for a few years and many countries still do not allow any operation on it. These countries employ frequencies within the band for their domestic television stations and are afraid of any possible interference to TV services. British Class A and B amateur licence holders can use any part of the 50 to 52MHz band but Novices are restricted to two segments: 50.620 to 50.760MHz and 51.250 to 51.750MHz. The first segment can only be used for data transmissions but the higher-frequency section allows Morse, telephony and data working.

The 433 to 435MHz Novice band is a small section of the 430 to 440MHz (70cm) amateur band. Radio amateurs are secondary users of this band and must co-exist with radars and military installations. The Novice allocation includes the British FM (frequency modulation) 'simplex' channels and the repeater frequencies.

50MHz can be used for local and semi-local working (ground wave) at all times but there are some occasions when there is extended propagation to far beyond 'normal' ranges.

Through the summer months in daylight hours 'Sporadic E' conditions are common and then it is possible to make contact with stations hundreds of miles away.

There are also less-frequent occasions when communication with amateurs thousands of miles away becomes possible. These times are usually around the periods of sunspot maximum when intense ionisation of the upper atmosphere will allow 'skip' propagation.

This is usually a propagation mode common to the HF bands and is rare on frequencies as high as 50MHz.

Another cause of extended range on 50MHz can be linked to weather conditions. Under certain conditions of high atmosphere pressure, signals can follow the surface of the earth much beyond the normal ground-wave range. This is called 'tropospheric propagation' or 'tropo' for short. The extended range can be up to a few hundred miles and is possible at any time of the year.

Further causes of extended range are auroral reflection and also reflections from meteorite trails. The many different possibilities for long-range working make the 50MHz band interesting and exciting.

There are fewer long-distance propagation opportunities when operating on the 434MHz band and these few will be because of extended 'tropo'. As previously mentioned, this depends upon weather conditions and is a phenomenon which often gives rise to foreign interference on our domestic TV sets. The 70cm band is fine for semi-local work on the 'simplex' channels or working through a repeater.

Many repeaters have been set up in the British Isles and they are particularly useful when operating from a moving motor vehicle. Repeaters can also be operated when low-powered, hand-held transceivers with very small antennas are used.

Dipoles for 50MHz

Many operators on this band use multi-element beams to enhance the signals from their quite low-powered transmitters (often 10W or less) but much can be achieved when using simple half-wave dipole antennas.

The author contacted an amateur in West Africa who was using 5W power and a wire dipole pushed out

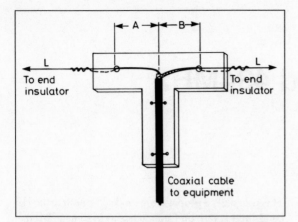

Fig 6.1. The centre connections for a 50MHz wire dipole. Accurate measurement is needed and the two dipole legs L must be 2.8m (9ft 2in) long. This length includes A or B which are the distances between the inner ends of the dipole wires and the body of the coaxial feeder

from his hotel window. This demonstrates that, when propagation conditions are good, exciting long-distance contacts can be made when using low-power transmitters and a simple dipole antenna.

A dipole will be about two 'S' (signal strength) points down on both transmit and receive when compared with a five-element beam, but this can be disregarded when conditions are really 'wide open' on 50MHz. Unfortunately, overseas stations may not operate on the frequencies allocated to British Novices, so a simple antenna will suffice and permit good communication with local and semi-local stations.

The directional properties of a dipole antenna (poor signal strengths off the ends) mean that for all-round coverage two dipoles positioned at right angles to each other must be used. The dipoles can be switched as shown in Fig 4.1 with a cheap knife switch. A coaxial switch would have less loss and give better matching to the 50Ω coaxial cable but can be an expensive item to purchase.

When dipoles are used on the VHF bands, care must be taken to ensure that their leg lengths are measured accurately.

The short distance between the coaxial cable and the connecting points at the antenna centre must be included as parts of the dipole length (Fig 6.1). To be resonant on 51MHz, which is a centre frequency for the Novice band, a half-wave dipole will have a total length of 2.8m (9ft 2in), each dipole leg being a half of this.

Wire dipoles can be located in the loft or roof space of a house but when this is done they should be kept well away from water tanks, pipes, wiring and other metallic objects.

A suitable balun (balance-to-unbalance device) for 50MHz dipoles will be described later.

A dipole which can be rotated to receive or transmit in different directions will be much better than a fixed antenna. Wire antennas are not easily arranged to rotate so elements made with aluminium tubing instead of wire should be used. The construction of a rotary dipole is made easier when a commercially available centre piece is used.

A typical example is illustrated in Fig 6.2 which is designed to take dipole legs made with 13mm (½in) diameter tube. It has a waterproof connection box and can be easily attached to a 25mm (1in) diameter mast. Each dipole leg will be 1.38m (4ft 6¼in) long and the distance between the tube ends and the coaxial cable will be 20mm (¾in) which, when added to the tube length, makes up the correct length for resonance on 51MHz.

The dipole centres are made from a strong black plastic material and can be obtained for fixing to either round- or square-section masts. Although reasonably waterproof, the connection box can be additionally protected from dampness by covering all the connections with a silicone rubber sealant. This can also be applied around the cable entry hole.

A very effective balun for a 50MHz dipole antenna can be made with ferrite beads (Fig 6.3). Suitable beads are available in a size which allows them to be slipped over a coaxial cable such as the standard RG58AU. Just six beads will be enough and they will take up a length of 28mm (1⅛in).

The beads are specially manufactured for use as 'slip on' baluns and may be obtained from Ferromagnetics of Mold in Clwyd (see Appendix 1). The beads have the part number FB-BLN FB-73 2401.

On the lower-frequency bands, ie between 1.9 and 28MHz, the manufacturers suggest that 50 beads should be used.

The beads are slipped over the coaxial cable before it is connected to the dipole centre and they should be positioned 3 or 4cm (1¼ to 1½in) from the top end of the feeder. They can then be held in place and covered with plastic insulating tape. The tape should then be itself held in place and protected against weathering with silicone rubber sealant.

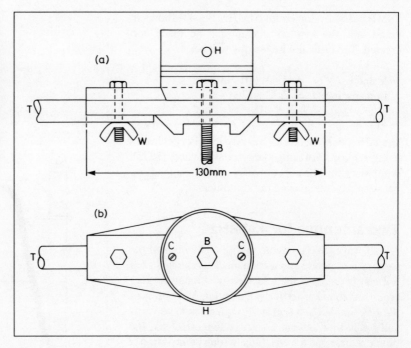

Fig 6.2. (a) A side elevation view of the dipole centre piece. Two wing-nuts W secure the aluminium tubes (T) and the bolt B is used to fix the dipole to a 25mm (1in) diameter mast or pole. A square-section mast would be needed with the example illustrated. H is the entry hole for the coaxial feeder. (b) Plan of the centre piece. The top of the securing bolt B is in the centre of the connection box. A similar dipole centre piece can be obtained from TAR Communications (see Appendix 1)

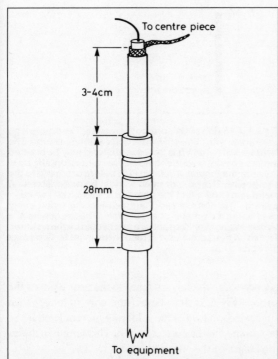

Fig 6.3. A balun for the 50MHz rotary dipole is made with six ferrite beads which are slipped over the coaxial cable. The beads are a good fit for RG58AU, UR43 or UR76 cables which all have an outside diameter of 5mm (0.195in)

The rotary dipole should be mounted as high as possible and well away from surrounding objects – the method for its rotation is best left to the ingenuity of the constructor. The author still uses manual rotation, known in some quarters as the 'Armstrong' method!

Making a beam antenna for the 50MHz band is rather difficult for a beginner so no designs are suggested. Multi-element beam antennas for the band may be purchased but they are not necessary for neighbourhood or semi-local contacts.

A vertical antenna for 50MHz

From 5 April 1991 British amateurs were allowed to use vertical polarisation in the 50MHz band. When the band was first opened to British amateurs it was feared that the use of vertical polarisation might give rise to interference with television transmissions in Europe (northern France and Belgium particularly). Many countries still employ Band 1 (which includes the 50MHz band) for their domestic TV services and often vertical antenna polarisation is used. The fears regarding interference proved unfounded and as a result there was a relaxation of licence conditions here.

Vertical polarisation is ideal for all-round local and semi-local communication on 50MHz, and the design for vertical antennas made with wire for use on 21 and

28MHz can be adopted for 51MHz. Fig 4.6 shows in detail how the vertical antenna can be made and erected. The critical wire lengths will be:

V and L   = 1.4m (4ft 7in)
End spacing D = 2.15m (7ft)

This design is quite small on the 51MHz band and should be positioned as high as possible. Feeder losses using standard 50Ω impedance coaxial cable (RG58 or similar) must be kept down by avoiding a long run between the antenna and the equipment.

Two antennas for 434MHz

A half-wave dipole having tubing elements and the same type of centre connection block as shown in Fig 6.2 can be constructed and then positioned to give either horizontal or vertical polarisation. Most users of the FM simplex and repeater frequencies have vertically polarised antennas, so it is suggested that the dipole is arranged for this. If the wrong polarisation is used the transmitted and received signal strengths will be low within the ground-wave range.

To make the dipole, the same length allowance at the centre feed point must be made as was suggested for the 50MHz dipole, ie 20mm, so each dipole leg will then have a length of 144mm (5¾in). The aluminium tube is also of the same diameter (13mm or ½in), because the commercial centre block is designed to take this tube size.

Standard 50Ω impedance coaxial cable becomes quite 'lossy' (ie there will be a loss of power in the cable) at 434MHz, so long runs of feeder cannot be made. It is suggested that cable lengths no greater than 10m (32ft) should be used. The feeder must run away at right angles from the dipole centre for at least 300mm (1ft) before it comes down vertically to the operating position (the equipment).

A balun made with just four of the ferrite beads described earlier may be used. Many operators do not use a balun on this type of antenna at VHF for they consider it is unnecessary. The complete 434MHz dipole antenna is shown in Fig 6.4.

A very simple, cheap, but effective ground-plane antenna can be made from wire and a standard SO239 chassis-mounting socket. This is the socket made to receive a PL259 plug. The vertical quarter-wave radiator is a 164mm (6½in) length of 16SWG hard-drawn

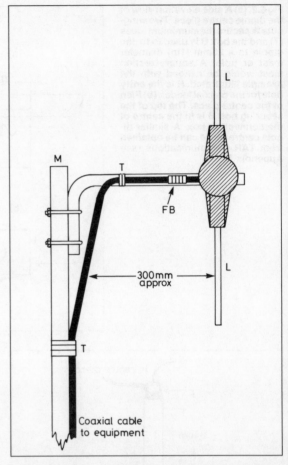

Fig 6.4. A 434MHz vertical dipole antenna. The dipole legs L are made with 13mm (½in) diameter aluminium tube. The ferrite-bead balun FB is not essential and may be omitted but the coaxial feeder should run back horizontally from the antenna for about 300mm (1ft) before dropping to the equipment. The pole or mast N must be non-metallic. A metal mast will affect the antenna's 'all round' radiation pattern. The ties marked T are self-locking nylon cable ties having a diameter of about 5mm. These each have a tensile strength of 22kg and are unaffected by the weather. The short horizontal tube is held to the mast by two small 'U' bolts

copper wire which is soldered to the centre pin of the socket (Fig 6.5). It is best if the wire is longer than suggested, and when the soldering is completed it can be trimmed to the correct length. This length includes the length of the connection pin.

The SO239 socket has a square base with four holes to take bolts at its corners, and these holes make convenient tie points for the ground-plane wires. Four pieces of 16SWG hard-drawn copper wire, each

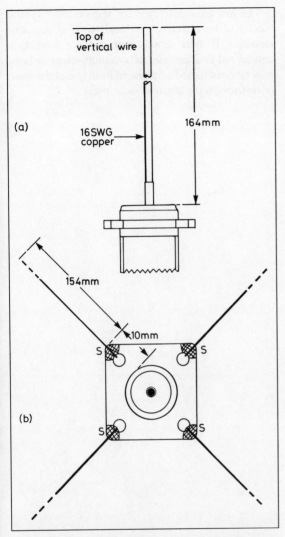

Fig 6.5. (a) How the 434MHz quarter-wave vertical radiator is soldered to the pin of an SO239 socket. (b) Plan view of the socket which shows the four radial wires. These are soldered to the socket mounting plate at each corner and are arranged to slope down at angle of about 40°

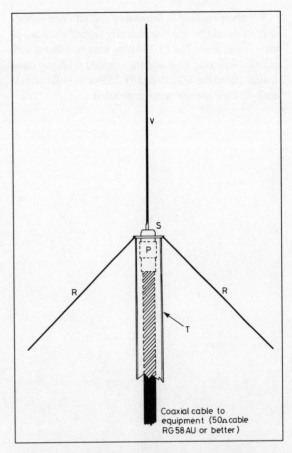

Fig 6.6. The complete 434MHz ground plane antenna. V is the vertical wire radiator and wires R are two of the four ground plane wires. The socket S and the PL259 plug fit inside a plastic pipe T and the feeder drops down through this pipe. It is suggested that a tight fit to the pipe can be made by wrapping the plug with insulating tape and then weatherproofing with a silicone rubber sealant

190mm (7½in) long, should be fixed securely at the four corner holes by bending over and squeezing with pliers. Before the four wires are soldered to the socket base, the latter should be filed or well rubbed with an emery paper then 'tinned' with solder. Each wire must be trimmed to a length of 154mm (6⅛in) when it is soldered in position. The distance between the outer corners of the socket and the central cylindrical barrel makes up the additional length to become a quarter wavelength for the band, ie 164mm.

To get the correct antenna feed impedance of 50Ω, the four ground plane wires must be bent downwards to an angle of about 40° from the horizontal. The actual angle may be adjusted later when the antenna is set up and working, and it will be correct when the lowest SWR is shown on the SWR meter in the feed line.

A suggested way to mount this antenna is by dropping the feeder with its PL259 plug down into a short length of rigid plastic tubing. 'Plumber's wastepipe' with a diameter of 21mm (0.85in) is fine for this, and a length of about 600mm (approximately 2ft) will be ideal. This short mast can then be secured to an existing mast or pole placed in a high open position (Fig 6.6).

Weatherproofing is important and silicone rubber sealant should be applied liberally around the base of the vertical wire. The PL259 plug may be wound with plastic insulating tape and then coated with the same sealant. Both the SO239 and PL259 units will corrode badly if they are not weatherproofed.

The antennas described for use on the 434MHz band will be effective for local working and with repeaters. If more serious long-distance working is considered at some later date, a multi-element beam may be constructed or obtained from one of the many advertisers in the amateur radio press.

Chapter 7

Ancillary equipment

Some easily constructed items of equipment can be built and used to make sure that there is the maximum transfer of transmitter power to the antenna system.

In this chapter two output indicators are described, one to be used with antennas fed by a coaxial cable and the other for use with end-fed wires. There is also some information on the use of a SWR meter. This device becomes very important when higher transmitter powers are used, for the output stages of some transmitters can be damaged or even destroyed if they are running at full power into an unmatched load.

A dummy load and power meter is also described. This unit will allow transmitter adjustments to be made without making 'on air' transmissions. It will also be useful to determine output power and thus keep within the terms of the Novice licence.

An output indicator for end-fed antennas

A simple output indicator which uses a meter to display relative power output to the antenna is shown in Fig 7.1.

The coils L1 and L2 are the two windings of an RF transformer which has a piece of ferrite rod as its core. L1 is a single turn of wire around the rod and L2 has four turns which can be moved towards or away from L1. The RF induced into L2 is rectified by the diode D which allows the use of a DC meter M. The capacitor C is an RF bypass across the meter.

Stiff 16 or 14SWG enamelled wire is used to make the transformer windings. L1 can have a few dabs of adhesive (UHU cement being ideal) to hold it in position but L2 can be moved towards or away from the secured single turn.

This indicator is very sensitive and, with a transmitter output of 3W, the author found that when L2 was

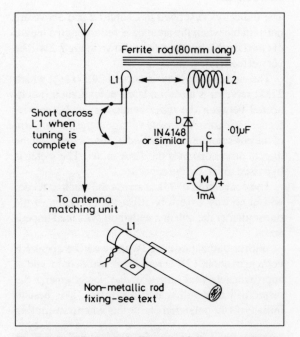

Fig 7.1. An RF output indicator which uses a meter to indicate the best tuning point. The coils L1 and L2 are wound over a short (80mm) piece of ferrite rod. If enamelled wire is not used for the coils, L2 may be wound on a close-fitting paper tube which can slide towards or away from L1. Almost any small silicon diode will perform well as D and the bypass capacitor C should be a disc ceramic component. This indicator can be set up to give useful meter readings at very low transmitter powers, certainly with powers below 0.5W

positioned well away from L1 there was enough rectified current to give full-scale readings on the 1mA movement meter. The same tuning procedure as outlined for the bulb indicator (Chapter 2) can be followed, and when the ideal tuning of the matcher is found the coil L1 may be shorted across.

A small baseboard can be used to mount the piece of ferrite rod with its coil windings, with a piece of copper-faced circuit board screwed to it to provide a panel for the meter. The ferrite rod is best held in position with a strap made from an insulating material.

Never fix a ferrite rod to a panel or board with a complete metallic single turn as it will then behave as a shorted one-turn coil. An examination of the fixing of the ferrite coil in a domestic transistor radio will reveal how the shorted coil problem is avoided.

An output indicator for coaxial-fed antennas

The indicators described in Chapter 2 and above are not suitable when the antenna is fed through a length of coaxial cable but the device shown in Fig 7.2 will be very effective.

The circuit shows a resistance of 24.2kΩ (of which 22kΩ represents a carbon track potentiometer) connected between the inner conductor of the coaxial feeder and earth. A variable voltage at the moving arm of the potentiometer is rectified by the diode D and the direct current operates the 1mA meter. The meter is bypassed to RF by the capacitor C.

The connection of 24kΩ across the antenna feeder will in no way adversely affect the operation of the transmitter or the antenna with their 50Ω feed impedances.

With an output power of 3W there will be a peak RF voltage of about 12V across the resistor chain, and at approximately mid-setting of the potentiometer the meter will read full scale. In practice, it is best to initially set the potentiometer so that when transmitting

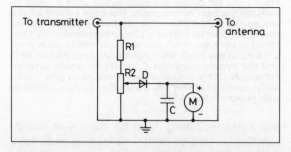

Fig 7.2. Circuit of an 'in-line' output indicator for use with antennas fed with coaxial cable. R1 is a non-inductive 2.2kΩ ½W resistor in series with a 22kΩ carbon track potentiometer rated at 0.4W and with a linear track. The diode D is a 1N4148 and the bypass capacitor is a disc ceramic type with a capacitance of 0.01µF (1nF) and a 50V voltage rating. The meter M is a moving coil unit with a full-scale deflection of 1mA

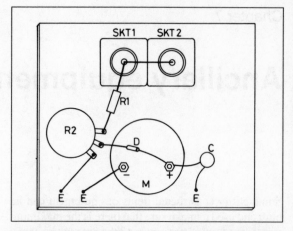

Fig 7.3. Plan view of the output indicator which has its components mounted on a double copper-faced board. The points marked E are solder connections to the copper board. SKT1 and SKT2 are chassis-mounting PL259 types. The wire connecting these sockets should be of 16 or 14SWG, insulated with plastic sleeving and pressed down to lie against the copper board. This will help to maintain the 50Ω impedance between the connectors

the meter reading is at half scale (0.5mA), and then transmitter adjustments to increase output can be easily seen.

This indicator unit is easily constructed and its component layout can take several forms. It is suggested that a piece of double-sided copper-surfaced circuit board be used as a front panel on which everything can be mounted. This panel can then be used as the front of a boxed enclosure or just screwed to a piece of wood which will act as a base. A completely enclosed version is more professional looking and will be dust free!

A suggested component arrangement on the board is shown in Fig 7.3.

The SWR meter

A simple one-meter SWR meter is shown in Fig 7.4. It is always connected between the transmitter and the ATU or antenna. It will only work correctly when its input and output impedances (50Ω) are connected to the same impedances at the transmitter and the ATU (or antenna).

An SWR (standing wave ratio) meter, or 'reflectometer' as it is sometimes called, is very useful in ensuring that an antenna is correctly matched to the transmitter. A ratio of 1:1 or close to this means that it

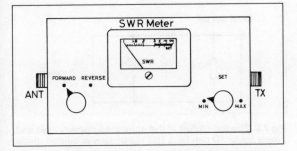

Fig 7.4. A single-meter SWR meter. Some SWR indicators use two meters, one to show forward power and the second to show reverse power (reflected power). Another type has a single meter with two pointer needles which are arranged to cross over. A standard SWR meter will only work correctly when it is used with a matched 50Ω impedance feeder

is, but a mismatch such as antenna impedances of 25Ω or 100Ω will give SWR readings of 2:1. This latter reading does not imply that the antenna will not work, but larger ratios might mean that the transmitter may suffer damage to its output stage.

Many modern transceivers will automatically reduce their output powers when a mismatch occurs. When using an SWR meter to set up an ATU, it is best to reduce the transmitter power output because adjustments of the ATU tuning can give rise to severe temporary mismatch.

An SWR meter of the type illustrated will have a control often marked as 'SET'. This can be adjusted so that the meter reading when the SWR meter is switched to 'FORWARD' is full scale. If the meter is then switched to 'REVERSE' some idea of the mismatch can be seen. The higher the meter reading the worse will be the SWR. The ATU controls must be adjusted to give the lowest possible meter reading when the SWR is set to 'REVERSE'.

Make sure that the correct SWR connectors go to the equipment and the ATU or antenna. These connectors are often marked 'ANT' and 'TX'; the latter obviously going via coaxial cable to the transmitter.

An SWR meter can be built at home but there are many cheap models on the market.

Those intended for use by the CB fraternity are inexpensive and suitable for Novice power levels.

The correct way to interconnect an SWR meter is shown in Fig 7.5.

A dummy load and power output meter

Whilst testing or adjusting a transmitter it should not be left connected to an antenna for more than a few seconds, for the radiation of unwanted signals is both anti-social and contrary to good amateur practice. The transmitter should instead be connected to a 'dummy load'. This is a 50Ω resistor which replaces the antenna and absorbs the transmitter power output.

Power resistors which can dissipate 3 or 4W without overheating or distress are usually wirewound components and are therefore unsuitable. The wire winding of the resistor has inductance and the load will not be truly resistive. Non-inductive resistors which have a suitable power rating are not generally available but, by using several low-wattage resistors, one can make up a suitable 50Ω load.

If eight 100Ω carbon film resistors, each with a 2W power rating, are connected as shown in Fig 7.6, they will make an effective 16W non-inductive load. As a result of having a rating of 16W, the resistors will not overheat if connected to a 3W output transmitter for quite long periods. Overheating can alter the value of dummy load resistors and they would not then match the 50Ω impedance of the transmitter.

The resistors are connected in series-parallel and

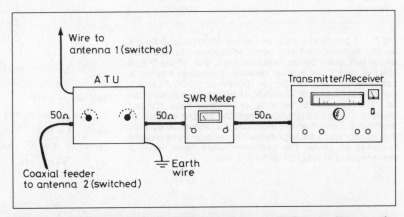

Fig 7.5. A typical station arrangement showing an SWR meter between the transmitter and the antenna system (usually via an ATU). The ATU shown can be switched to connect to coaxial-fed antennas or single-wire antennas

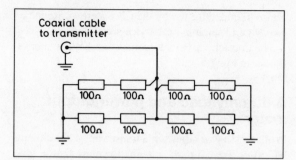

Fig 7.6. The circuit for a transmitter dummy load which uses eight 100Ω resistors in series-parallel to give an overall resistance of 50Ω at the coaxial socket

each has a length of 23mm and a diameter of 8mm. They can be bought as having a resistance value within ±5% of their nominal value.

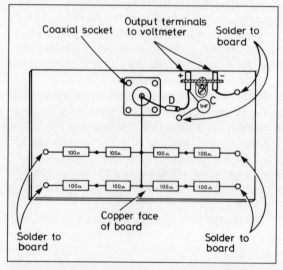

Fig 7.7. A practical layout on copper-faced circuit board for the dummy load and some additional components which will allow power measurement. The diode D is a 1N4148 and C is a disc ceramic capacitor having a capacitance value of 1nF (or 1000pF or 0.001µF) and a working voltage of at least 50V. The output terminals can be a short section of 'tag strip' or a similar item. The tag marked '+' must be insulated from the copper surface of the board. Except where indicated as 'solder to board', the resistor leads are kept above the surface. For accurate readings of power the voltmeter used must have a movement of at least 20,000Ω per volt

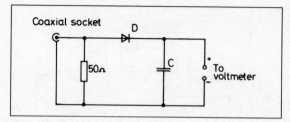

Fig 7.8. The full circuit of the combined dummy load and power meter. D can be a 1N4148 or similar silicon diode

A suitable arrangement on a piece of copper-faced circuit board is shown in Fig 7.7.

The dummy load can also be used as part of a power output meter to an accuracy of 10% when used in the circuit shown in Fig 7.8. In this circuit the diode D rectifies the RF voltage. The capacitor C charges to peak voltage and also acts as an RF bypass. If a good voltmeter with a movement of at least 20,000Ω per volt is used to measure the voltage across the output terminals, a fair estimate of the power output of the transmitter can be made.

The voltage value must be squared and divided by 100. This will give the average power into the dummy load.

Here are some worked examples:

7V	=	0.5W
8.5V	=	0.72W
10.0V	=	1.00W
12.5V	=	1.56W
14.0V	=	2.00W
16.0V	=	2.50W
17.5V	=	3.00W
19.0V	=	2.50W
20.0V	=	4.00W

This dummy load and power meter can be used on any of the Novice bands, although the accuracy will fall off at VHF.

The power meter was described by D Plumridge, G3KMG, in the G-QRP Club magazine *Sprat* in the summer of 1986, and derived from an original article by the American amateur Ade Weiss, K8EEG.

Chapter 8

Safety and commonsense

Amateur radio is a safe hobby. It is certainly much safer than many outdoor pursuits. The activities of fishing, athletics, sailing or even the mundane tasks of gardening often result in injury or sometimes death (36,000 reported gardening accidents each year in Britain). No human activity is absolutely safe but when sensible precautions are taken the likelihood of falling victim to accident is greatly reduced.

It is hoped that this chapter will assist the Novice radio amateur in avoiding the few dangers that can arise when actively pursuing the hobby. These dangers concern not just the Novice but also involve his or her family, friends and neighbours.

Mains electricity supplies

A low-powered amateur station can be powered from batteries, but this can be rather expensive when the batteries are of the 'use and then discard' types. Rechargeable batteries are more economical but a mains supply is needed to power their charger. Many amateurs prefer to power their equipment from a low-voltage (6 to 24V) supply derived from a mains-energised power pack and this is just about the cheapest way to operate from a home station (neglecting of course the free power that can be obtained from solar energy).

Most homes have a 240V AC supply which has 'live', 'neutral' and 'earth' wiring arranged on a ring main system with three-pin outlet sockets. It is essential that all mains-powered equipment and tools such as soldering irons or drills that have exposed metal parts are correctly earthed via the larger pin on the mains plugs.

A wise scheme is to have one master switch or plug, preferably located outside the operating room or 'shack' which can be used to remove all mains power from that room. This switch or plug can be red-coloured and for an additional safeguard can have a neon lamp that will glow when the power is 'on'. Switches and plugs are available which have built-in neon lamps.

Your family should be shown this switch and instructed to switch it off immediately should there be any electrical problem to do with amateur radio operations. This might include fire when a faulty equipment overheats and has not 'blown' its fuse correctly. This state of affairs should never happen if the correct fuse ratings are used but there are the rare occasions when fuses do not 'blow' in time. If the operating room has another use as a bedroom etc, the master switch may then be located inside the room.

Most of the equipment used by the Novice will be rated below 240W of power so it is suggested that each three-pin power plug should have a fuse with a 3A rating.

Protective multiple earthing (PME)

A growing number of properties, especially new houses or flats and also many re-wired older houses, do not use the older earthing system just described. Instead they have the 'neutral' conductor wire connected to 'earth'. When this is done, every item of plumbing, including gas pipes, radiators, boilers, washing machines etc, must be bonded (connected) to the 'neutral' conductor wire at the fuse-box. This is a very safe system when you are inside the house for everything is 'equipotential' (at the same voltage), but there is a potential danger if you have an independent outside earth connection for your radio equipment.

Before setting up your home radio station it is therefore best to ask advice regarding your mains supply system from your local Electricity Board or a competent electrician.

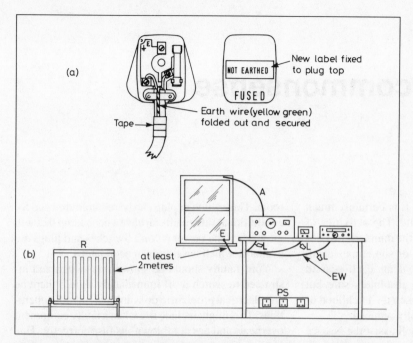

Fig 8.1. (a) How each power plug in the radio room must have its earth wire disconnected and tied back with tape when the home has protective multiple earthing (PME) electrical wiring. A 'NOT EARTHED' label must be fixed securely to each power plug. (b) The power sockets are best placed near the operating position and the earth wire to each piece of equipment must carry a label L marked 'SAFETY EARTH – DO NOT REMOVE'. The main earth lead E goes out at the bottom of the window. There MUST be a distance of AT LEAST 2m (6ft) between the main earth, the equipment earth wires EW and any metal appliances R, such as radiators or heaters, that are bonded to the PME system. The antenna wire A is taken out at the top of the window

Outside earths have been specified for many of the antennas described in these chapters so if you live in a building where there is PME certain precautions *must* be taken. The danger may arise should there be a fault in the electricity supply involving a break in the 'neutral' wiring. Without going into detail, this means that if such a break happened and you were unaware of it there could be a high-voltage potential between your radio earth and any of the bonded appliances within reach. Any voltage higher than about 34V can be dangerous so the unexpected high voltage between your earth system and a radiator or other item in the room could prove lethal.

A recommended way to remove the danger that might arise with a PME system is to disconnect the earth wire (yellow/green) from every three-pin mains plug in the radio room and loop them back from the plugs and tape them down to the lead. A clear label *must* then be put on each plug which says 'NOT EARTHED'. The metal cases or chassis of each piece of radio equipment (even battery-powered equipment) must then be connected to the radio earth which goes to the ground outside. Any wire thus connecting the equipment with the outside earth *must* carry a label which states 'SAFETY EARTH – DO NOT REMOVE'.

It must also be arranged that nothing that has been bonded in the PME system such as radiators or portable electrical equipment (kettles, fires and other heaters) comes within 2m (6ft) of the radio equipment or the outside earth wires. If this is done it will be absolutely impossible to simultaneously touch the PME earthing (supply 'earth' plus 'neutral') and the earthed radio gear (see Fig 8.1).

Even when your antenna is a dipole which does not need an earth connection there is always the possibility that it may unavoidably fall to the ground and be earthed. If this happens, its coaxial feeder which connects to your equipment will earth that equipment.

The possible dangers when PME systems are used must be placed into context. It is uncommon for a break to occur in the supply 'neutral' line but it can and sometimes does happen, so for absolute safety the measures outlined *must be followed*.

Protective multiple earthing has been in use for about 20 years and to date the author has never learned of any fatality or injury to any British amateur that was brought about by the system. Don't be the first unfortunate to fall victim, and take the precautions suggested.

Lightning protection

This can be an emotive topic which frequently frightens newcomers to the radio hobby. If sensible and quite simple precautions are taken there should be no

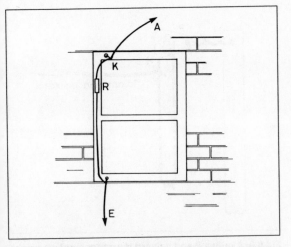

Fig 8.2. The wirewound resistor is connected (soldered) to the antenna wire A and the main earth downlead OUTSIDE the window. A bend or kink K in the antenna lead stops rainwater running down into the room

need to worry about possible death and destruction! A direct lightning strike on your property is unlikely and is something that cannot be prevented, but the gradual build-up of static electricity on antennas when thunderstorms are not in your immediate area can be avoided and the sensitive, easily damaged components in your equipment can be safeguarded.

The higher and the longer a wire antenna is, the more likely it is to acquire static electrical charges. The author has for years used a simple method of draining away static charges on his outside wires which involves the use of just one cheap component. This is a 10W wirewound resistor, outside the operating room window, that connects between the antenna wire and the earth wire. A resistor with a value of 33,000Ω will be effective and will not reduce the efficiency of the antenna. A wirewound resistor has inductance and will therefore also act as an RF choke and be effective in isolating the antenna from earth (see Fig 8.2) at radio frequencies, but not prevent the discharge of static voltages.

The downlead to earth must be as thick, as short and as straight as possible; lightning does not like to go around corners! When the equipment is not in use it is a good idea to connect the antenna to earth directly with a thick wire. *Never* touch an antenna wire when a thunderstorm is in progress or is likely.

It is best to be somewhat fatalistic about lightning, for despite taking normal precautions one cannot

prevent a direct strike. Just when and where it may strike cannot be predicted and it may be any item of architecture or metalwork. It is commonsense to stop operating, switch off and earth the antennas if electrical storms are approaching.

Radio-frequency radiation hazards

This subject is still being researched but some conclusions have already been agreed by scientists. It seems that at amateur power levels (up to 400W peak power) on the HF bands there is little to worry about.

It is when working with transmitters on the VHF and UHF bands that more care must be taken. On the 70cm (434MHz) band the typical short 'rubber duck' antenna of a hand-held transceiver must never be held near the eyes. There is a small chance that even a few watts of RF energy on this frequency may start the medical condition of cataract. The length of permissible exposure and the actual powers needed are not known so it is suggested that, when transmitting from a hand-held UHF transceiver, the antenna should be positioned as far as possible from the face.

The author has operated with high-powered transmitters on most of the amateur bands for more than 45 years and to date has not suffered attributable health problems. Your Novice power limit of 3W output can, I feel sure, be used with little fear of damage to health.

Wires everywhere!

Experimenting with antennas is fascinating for most radio amateurs, but sometimes one can be over-zealous and forget some aspects of safety. Low drooping wires are unsightly and also potentially dangerous. This is particularly the case when they are at head or neck level and could cause serious injury to a forgetful or unsuspecting relative or neighbour. A visitor or neighbour could sue the operator if they suffered any injury from badly positioned wires.

Counterpoise wires close to the ground can be a hazard, and if set out they must be placed away from paths and places used frequently. The author has several hundreds of feet of counterpoise wires but they cannot be seen or tripped over. They are all secreted inside boundary hedges or tacked to fencing.

The far end of an antenna wire will have high RF voltages present even when the transmitter power is small. Just a few watts can give unpleasant shocks or

RF burns to the unwary, so keep the ends of all wire antennas well above the ground where they cannot be touched by humans or animals. Birds can sit on antenna wires and come to no harm even when quite high power levels are being used, for they have no connection to earth.

Coaxial feeders may be buried or arranged to run along the property boundaries. This will not be necessary if the antenna is close to the operating position and the feeder can then drop straight down to a window or other inlet point.

Wire antennas must not go over neighbouring properties unless written permission has been obtained, for there is always the unwelcome occasion when something breaks and the wires come down together with insulators and other hardware.

Overhead power lines are a common feature in rural areas and they present a particular threat to the amateur antenna maker. All antennas must be kept well away from power lines and arranged so that they cannot fall across them at any time. Power lines carry a lot of electrical noise so it is always best to position your antenna as far away from them as possible.

The positioning of an antenna must be a compromise between efficiency and safety. Telephone wires must be avoided, too, for they often result in screening effects and also some modern telephones will pick up amateur transmissions if the wires are not well separated.

Insurance cover can be obtained against the possibility of claims against amateurs arising from antenna mishaps, and such a policy is available to RSGB members at reasonable cost.

Working on antennas

Antennas should be arranged to be as high as possible and well away from any screening influences such as buildings or trees. Amateurs often need to raise and lower their wires frequently to make adjustments or modifications, so it is not a good idea to fix them permanently to convenient tie points.

Pulleys and continuous loop halyards will allow the rapid raising and lowering of wires, and should be used whenever possible. A pulley and halyard system is shown in Fig 8.3. Try to get good-quality marine pulleys. They are not cheap but they will not corrode or seize when out of doors in all winds and weathers for many years. Two good pulleys will do away with

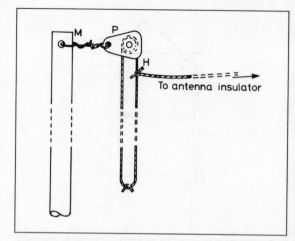

Fig 8.3. A pulley P and halyard H arrangement where the halyard rope is a continuous loop. The pulley must be securely fixed to the mast M or some other tie point

the need for frequent climbing to make antenna adjustment.

Clambering on roofs and climbing trees is very dangerous and should only be done by professionals. For a modest sum a TV antenna fitter will speedily and efficiently fix a mast to your chimney stack or other suitable feature of your house. He will have and use the correct equipment, will be insured against accident and can advise on the safety of the installation.

When a pulley has to be placed high in a tree, a recognised expert or 'tree surgeon' should be contacted, for tree climbing is even more dangerous than working on roofs.

If it is decided to erect a mast, at least two people are needed. When the mast is heavier or longer than a thin-walled aluminium tube (sectional) with a total length of 10m (32ft), more hands are needed. A 15m (50ft) mast may need five helpers for its safe erection and require special techniques covered in more advanced publications.

Masts need support guys and these can be good-quality sailing ship rigging. Suitable ropes can be brought at a chandlers or sailing gear shop. Pulley halyards should also be made from similar ropes. Good ropes will last for many years despite the effects of sunlight and dampness.

It is possible to put up antennas and do no climbing at all but often some height will be sacrificed. A thin line may be first thrown over a roof ridge and used to pull over a heavier antenna support cord. Similarly a cord can be thrown over a tree branch.

The author uses a 'secret weapon' for his throwing activities! This is a ball of modelling clay or plasticine on the end of a thin (1mm diameter) 'non-kink' nylon string tied to a piece of 'lolly stick' inside the ball. With practice this device can be thrown well up into a tree. The weight of the ball will bring it down to the ground when it has gone across a bough. A heavier rope is then pulled over which will secure a pulley. Some care is needed when following this technique for it is easy to break a window with a 50mm diameter ball of plasticine. The ball can also be used to get the support cord over a roof ridge, and in this case the hazard will be any windows on the unseen side of the house.

Trees have considerable movement in rough weather so allowance must be made for this when fixing an antenna to a branch. A weighted halyard (Fig 8.4) is one way to overcome this problem.

If a ladder is used, inexperienced climbers should not attempt work with one longer than 3m (10ft) and then there must be someone else at its foot to steady it and give confidence.

A useful item when doing antenna work is a 4m (12ft) pole. The author uses one made from a pair of interlocking aluminium tubes and it has often saved many climbing attempts.

Most antennas require soldered connections and these should be made indoors or close to the house. Mains-powered soldering irons should not be used in a garden unless a sensitive circuit breaker is in the power line. A low-voltage soldering iron is safer but it

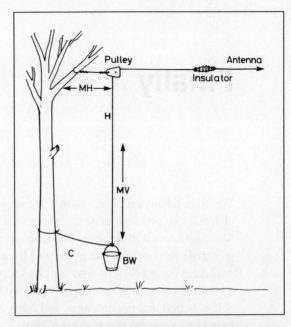

Fig 8.4. Trees and branches move a great deal in windy weather. This horizontal movement MH will put a great strain upon an antenna wire, but if a weight is suspended at the lower end of the halyard this will then ride up and down (vertical movement MV) in bad weather. The weight may be a small plastic pail or bucket BW containing small stones and having drainage holes. The weight is adjusted for correct antenna tension. The short cord C will stop violent swings of the weight

will need very thick leads if more than a few metres of cable are used. Most antennas can be measured, made up and then brought to the house for soldering.

Finally . . .

We all need advice or assistance at times, and the Novice certainly will. When any difficulty or problem arises, always seek help from an experienced radio amateur. Most amateurs will be pleased to help and a few words of advice which may only take minutes can overcome many hours of frustration. If you join your local radio club, you will meet other Novices who will be facing the same problems as yourself and also a band of keen enthusiasts who can give valuable advice.

It is hoped that the antennas and other items described in this book will be of real help to newcomers to our great hobby. There are lots of other antennas waiting to be tried and tested and at some later date you will be able to benefit from more advanced publications. Learning about antennas holds a fascination for the author and it is a subject where there is always something new to make up and test. Have luck on the bands and "Safe and happy antenna farming!"

Appendix 1

List of suppliers

Here is a list of some suppliers of wire, components and other 'oddments' needed to make the antennas and items of equipment described in this book. There are of course other firms able to supply the parts needed, and it is suggested that the advertising columns of amateur radio magazines should be closely studied.

J Birkett, 25 The Strait, Lincoln, LN2 1JF
Air-spaced variable capacitors and a wide range of small components for the amateur can be supplied.

Cirkit Distribution Ltd, Park Lane, Broxbourne, Herts, EN10 7NQ and **Maplin Electronics plc, PO Box 3, Rayleigh, Essex, SS6 8LR**
Both these firms are large mail-order organisations and have catalogues describing an enormous range of components and useful antenna hardware, including knife switches.

Dee Comm Amateur Radio Products, Unit 1A, Canal View Industrial Estate, Brettell Lane, Brierley Hill, West Midlands, DY5 3LQ
Aluminium and steel sectional antenna masts, guy rope kits, VHF antennas, wall brackets and bolts, rope, wire and other antenna hardware.

Ferromagnetics, PO Box 577, Mold, Clywd, North Wales, CH7 1AH
All kinds of ferrite components, such as rings, rods and beads, are supplied by this specialist firm.

Radio Society of Great Britain, Lambda House, Cranborne Road, Potters Bar, Herts, EN6 3JE
The RSGB can supply ferrite rings and a wide range of filters for combatting breakthrough and other EMC problems. All items may be purchased by members at a reduced price.

The Scientific Wire Company, 811 Forest Road, London, E17
As its name suggests, this firm stocks an enormous range of enamelled, silver-plated and tinned copper wires.

Tandy
These franchised electronics retailers have outlets in many towns, and can supply a wide range of parts such as coaxial cables and plugs, nylon cable ties, copper-faced circuit board, solder and wire etc.

TAR Communications, King William Street, Amblecote, Stourbridge, West Midlands, DY8 4EY
All kinds of antenna 'bits and pieces', wire, coaxial cable and ready-made antennas are supplied by this firm. A wide range of antenna masts is also stocked.

W H Westlake, West Park, Clawton, Holsworthy, Devon, EX22 6QN
A large range of cables and connectors, wire, insulators, solder, and the Swedish Bofa 300W impedance slotted feeder.

Pulleys, non-rot ropes and cords are best obtained from shops which specialise in gear for sailing enthusiasts. They are often located on the coast or close to inland waterways, canals and lakes. Suitable ropes and cords are often found in good ironmongers' shops and 'surplus' stores. Glues and silicone-rubber sealants are stocked by most of the DIY stores.

Most suppliers will send illustrated catalogues on receipt of a stamped addressed envelope. This will not apply in the case of Cirkit and Maplin which have very large catalogues on sale at W H Smith and other stationers.

The author has found that most suppliers will readily answer queries regarding their products and, if asked, will offer useful advice. Should it prove difficult to locate any particular item, the advice of an experienced radio amateur can be sought. Most amateurs are most willing to assist newcomers to the hobby.

Appendix 2

Suggested further reading

Antenna Notebook by Doug DeMaw, W1FB. Published by the American Radio Relay League (ARRL).

Novice Antenna Notebook by Doug DeMaw, W1FB. Published by the ARRL.

Practical Wire Antennas by John D Heys, G3BDQ. Published by the RSGB.

Simple, Low Cost Wire Antennas by William Orr, W6SAI, and Stuart D Cowan, W2LX. Published by Radio Publications Inc in the USA.

These titles may all be obtained from the RSGB. Members may purchase them at a reduced price.

Index

51

Some other RSGB publications...

❏ AMATEUR RADIO AWARDS

Gives details of major amateur radio awards throughout the world. Each award is listed in an easy-to-understand format, giving all the information on how to achieve it, and checklists are provided so that the amateur can keep a record of progress.

❏ AMATEUR RADIO TECHNIQUES

Basically an ideas and source book, this ever-popular work brings together a large selection of novel antennas, circuits and devices, together with many fault-finding and constructional hints.

❏ HF ANTENNA COLLECTION

An invaluable compendium of outstanding articles and short pieces which were published in *Radio Communication* during 1968 to 1989. As well as ingenious designs for single-element, beam and miniature antennas, there is a wealth of information on ancillary topics such as feeders, tuners, baluns, testing, modelling, and the mechanics of mounting an antenna safely.

❏ HF ANTENNAS FOR ALL LOCATIONS

This book explains the 'why' as well as the 'how' of HF antennas, and takes a look at existing designs in the light of the latest developments. An essential reference for the experimenter and enthusiast.

❏ PRACTICAL WIRE ANTENNAS

Wire antennas offer one of the most cost-effective ways to put out a good signal on the HF bands, and this practical guide to their construction has something to interest every amateur on a budget. Theory has been kept to a minimum – instead, the author has shared his years of experience in this field.

❏ GREAT CIRCLE DX MAP

Invaluable for the HF operator using a beam antenna, this map shows the true bearing and distance of any DX station on the globe from London. Also shown are world time zones, latitude and longitude and amateur radio prefixes. The *Great Circle DX Map* measures approximately 550mm square.

❏ WORLD PREFIX MAP

This is a superb multi-coloured wall map measuring approximately 1200 by 830mm. It shows amateur radio country prefixes worldwide, world time zones, IARU locator grid squares, and much more. A must for the shack wall of every radio amateur and listener.

 RADIO SOCIETY OF GREAT BRITAIN
Lambda House, Cranborne Road,
Potters Bar, Herts EN6 3JE

RSGB – *representing amateur radio ... ... representing you!*

Radio Communication

A magazine which covers a wide range of interests and which features the best and latest amateur radio news. The Society's journal has acquired a world-wide reputation for its content. It strives to maintain its reputation as the best available and is now circulated, free of charge, to members in over 150 countries.

The regular columns in the magazine cater for HF, VHF/UHF, microwave, SWL, clubs, satellite, data and contests. In addition to technical articles, the highly regarded 'Technical Topics' feature caters for those wishing to keep themselves briefed on recent developments in technical matters. There is also a special column for Novice licensees.

The 'Last Word' is a lively feature in which members can put forward their views and opinions and be sure of receiving a wide audience. To keep members in touch with what's going on in the hobby, events diaries are published each month.

Subsidised advertisements for the equipment you wish to sell can be placed in the magazine, with the advantages of short deadlines and large circulation.

QSL Bureau

Members enjoy the use of the QSL Bureau free of charge for both outgoing and incoming cards. This can save you a good deal of postage.

Special Event Callsigns

Special Event Callsigns in the GB series are handled by RSGB. They give amateurs special facilities for displaying amateur radio to the general public.

Specialised News Sheets

The Society publishes the weekly *DX News-sheet* for HF enthusiasts and the *Microwave Newsletter* for those operating above 1GHz.

Specialised Equipment Insurance

Insurance for your valuable equipment which has been arranged specially for members. The rates are very advantageous.

Audio Visual Library

Films, audio and video tapes are available through one of the Society's Honorary Officers for all affiliated groups and clubs.

Reciprocal Licensing Information

Details are available for most countries on the RSGB computer database.

Government Liaison

One of the most vital features of the work of the RSGB is the ongoing liaison with the UK Licensing Authority – presently the Radiocommunications Agency of the Department of Trade and Industry. Setting and maintaining the proper framework in which amateur radio can thrive and develop is essential to the well-being of amateur radio. The Society spares no effort in defence of amateur radio's most precious assets – the amateur bands.

Beacons and Repeaters

The RSGB supports financially all repeaters and beacons which are looked after by the appropriate committee of the Society, ie, 1.8-30MHz by the HF Committee, 30-1000MHz (1GHz) by the VHF Committee and frequencies above 1GHz by the Microwave Committee. For repeaters, the Society's Repeater Management Group has played a major role. Society books such as the *Amateur Radio Call Book* give further details, and computer-based lists giving up-to-date operational status can be obtained by post from HQ.

Operating Awards

A wide range of operating awards are available via the responsible officers: their names can be found in the front pages of *Radio Communication* and in the Society's *Amateur Radio Call Book*. The RSGB also publishes a book which gives details of most major awards.

Contests (HF/VHF/Microwave)

The Society has two contest committees which carry out all work associated with the running of contests. The HF Contests Committee deals with contests below 30MHz, whilst events on frequencies above 30MHz are dealt with by the VHF Contests Committee.

Morse Testing

In April 1986 the Society took over responsibility for morse testing of radio amateurs in the UK. If you wish to take a morse test, write direct to RSGB HQ (Morse tests) for an application form.

Slow Morse

Many volunteers all over the country give up their time to send slow morse over the air to those who are preparing for the 5 and 12 words per minute morse tests. The Society also produces morse instruction tapes.

RSGB Books

The Society publishes a range of books for the radio amateur and imports many others. RSGB members are entitled to a discount on all books purchased from the Society. This discount can offset the cost of membership.

Propagation

The Society's Propagation Studies Committee is highly respected – both within the amateur community and professionally – for its work. Predictions are given in the weekly GB2RS news bulletins and the Society's monthly magazine *Radio Communication*.

Technical and EMC Advice

Although the role of the Society's Technical and Publications Advisory Committee is largely to vet material intended for publication, its members and HQ staff are always willing to help with any technical matters.

Breakthrough in domestic entertainment equipment can be a difficult problem to solve as well as having licensing implications. The Society's EMC Committee is able to offer practical assistance in many cases. The Society also publishes a special book to assist you. Additional advice can be obtained from the EMC Committee Chairman via RSGB HQ.

Planning Permission

There is a special booklet and expert help available to members seeking assistance with planning matters.

GB2RS

A special radio news bulletin transmitted each week and aimed especially at the UK radio amateur and short wave listener. The script is prepared each week by the Society's HQ staff. The transmission schedule for GB2RS is printed regularly in *Radio Communication*, or it can be obtained via the Membership Services Department at HQ. It also appears in the *Amateur Radio Call Book*. The GB2RS bulletin is also sent out over the packet radio network.

Raynet (Radio Amateur Emergency Network)

Several thousand radio amateurs give up their free time to help with local, national and sometimes international emergencies. There is also ample opportunity to practise communication and liaison skills at non-emergency events, such as county shows and charity walks, as a service to the people. For more information or full details of how to join, contact the Membership Services Department at RSGB HQ.

RSGB Exhibitions and Mobile Rallies

The Society's Exhibition and Rally Committee organizes an annual exhibition and an annual mobile rally. Full details and rally calendar can be found in *Radio Communication*.

RSGB Conventions

The Society's diary in *Radio Communication* contains details of all special conventions which are open to all radio amateurs. The Society holds several major conventions each year.

Observation Service

A number of leading national radio societies have volunteers who monitor the amateur bands as a service to the amateur community. Their task is to spot licence infringements and defective transmissions, and report them in a friendly way to the originating station.

Intruder Watch

This helps to protect the exclusive amateur bands by monitoring for stations not authorised to use them.

Send for our Membership Information Pack today and discover how you too can benefit from these services. Write to:

RADIO SOCIETY OF GREAT BRITAIN, Lambda House, Cranborne Road, Potters Bar, Herts EN6 3JE

Notes

18 SWG .048" – 1.22mm (57M – 190FT)

21 mm pipe.

PRACTICAL ANTENNAS FOR NOVICES (1st edn)

We hope you found this book interesting and useful. Please let us have your comments
and suggestions for the next edition so we can make it even better!

Name..   Callsign...................................

Address..

....

....

....